A JUDGE CALLED DEBORAH

THE CALLED
BOOK 4

KENNETH A. WINTER

JOIN MY READERS' GROUP FOR UPDATES AND FUTURE RELEASES

Please join my Readers' Group so i can send you a free book, as well as updates and information about future releases, etc.

See the back of the book for details on how to sign up.

A Judge Called Deborah

"The Called" - Book 4 (a series of novellas)

Published by:

Kenneth A. Winter

WildernessLessons, LLC

Richmond, Virginia

United States of America

kenwinter.org

wildernesslessons.com

Edited by Sheryl Martin Hash

Cover design by Scott Campbell Design

ISBN 978-1-9568660-2-5 (soft cover)

ISBN 978-1-9568660-3-2 (e-book)

ISBN 978-1-9568660-4-9 (large print)

Library of Congress Control Number: 2022904324

DEDICATION

To LaVonne,
for your constant prayers,
your enduring strength,
your abiding faith,
your unending encouragement, and
your steadfast love … for me … our family … and our Lord

~

Who can find a virtuous and capable wife?
She is more precious than rubies.
Her husband can trust her,
and she will greatly enrich his life.
She brings him good, not harm,
all the days of her life.
Proverbs 31:10-12

~

CONTENTS

FROM THE AUTHOR

A word of explanation for those of you who are new to my writing.

You will notice that whenever i use the pronoun "I" referring to myself, i have chosen to use a lowercase "i." This only applies to me personally (in the Preface). i do not impose my personal conviction on any of the characters in this book. It is not a typographical error. i know this is contrary to proper English grammar and accepted editorial style guides. i drive editors (and "spell check") crazy by doing this. But years ago, the Lord convicted me – personally – that in all things i must decrease and He must increase.

And as a way of continuing personal reminder, from that day forward, i have chosen to use a lowercase "i" whenever referring to myself. Because of the same conviction, i use a capital letter for any pronoun referring to God throughout the entire book. The style guide for the New Living Translation (NLT) does not share that conviction. However, you will see that i have intentionally made that slight revision and capitalized any pronoun referring to God in my quotations of Scripture from the NLT. If i have violated any style guides as a result, please accept my apology, but i must honor this conviction.

Lastly, regarding this matter – this is a personal conviction – and i share it only so you will understand why i have chosen to deviate from normal editorial practice. i am in no way suggesting or endeavoring to have anyone else subscribe to my conviction. Thanks for your understanding.

PREFACE

~

This fictional novella is the fourth book in a series titled, *The Called,* which is about ordinary people whom God called to use in extraordinary ways. We tend to elevate the people we read about in Scripture and place them on a pedestal far beyond our reach. We often think, "Of course God used them. They had extraordinary strength or extraordinary faith. But God could never use an ordinary person like me."

But nothing could be further from the truth. The reality is that throughout history God has used the ordinary to accomplish the extraordinary – and He has empowered them through His Holy Spirit.

In the days that followed the leadership of Moses and Joshua, the people of Israel repeatedly turned their backs on God and went their own way. Their sin inevitably led to their captivity by a foreign king who treated them cruelly. Each time, by His grace, God mercifully responded to His people's cries for help and raised up judges to lead them out of their captivity and back to Him. This is the story of one of those judges – an Ephraimite woman named Deborah.

Though she lived in a day when the culture dictated that women were to be seen and not heard, God raised up this woman of faith, wisdom, and courage to lead her people as a prophetess and the fourth judge over Israel. She courageously rallied her people to go up against one of the best-trained and best-equipped armies of the day because of her confidence in the Lord God Jehovah.

Though God chose her to be a leader for Israel, Deborah did not seek fame or recognition. Rather, she had the humility and wisdom to choose a respected warrior by the name of Barak to be the commander over the armies of Israel. God gave her the discernment to know He would raise up another woman named Jael to, in fact, become the champion of Israel in the ultimate defeat of their powerful enemy.

In these pages, i will endeavor to unfold the stories of each of these people so we can see how their lives were divinely linked for that moment in history. i do so to help us see them as real people God used through their unique circumstances in extraordinary ways.

i hope you will sit back and get to know each one as we walk through their lives. Most of the characters in the story come directly from Scripture. You will recognize them from the pages of the early chapters in the Book of Judges. In numerous instances, i have chosen to add background details about them that are not found in Scripture. i draw heavily on the historical writings of Josephus and the Jewish historical traditions passed down through rabbinical teachings. But please remember that some of the elements i have added are plausible fiction.

One fictional device i have used is Deborah's family tree as it unfolds through the story. Though many of the individuals introduced are real people, i have crafted fictional family relationships to introduce the era of the judges in Israelite history into the story. As in my other stories, i have also added fictional characters to round out the narrative. i have included a character map as an appendix in the back of the book to clarify the historical and fictional elements of each character.

Throughout the story, some instances of dialogue are direct quotes from Scripture – these will be italicized. The Scripture references are included in a bibliography in the back of the book. Dialogue not italicized is part of the fictional story that helps advance the narrative.

Finally, my prayer is that as you read this story, you will see Deborah through new eyes – and be challenged to live out your walk with the Lord with the same boldness, humility, and courage she displayed. And most importantly, i pray you will be challenged to be an "ordinary" follower with the willingness and faith to be used by God in extraordinary ways … for His glory!

1

JOSHUA IS DEAD

~

Joshua has been dead for many years. He was God's chosen leader over our people for the thirty years leading up to his death. God's anointing on him had been conspicuous. Moses had mentored him for the prior forty years to prepare him to step into his leadership role. The succession in leadership had been well-planned, and the transition between the two men had gone smoothly.

Joshua was a wise and effective leader. God clearly spoke to him, and he knew how to hear from God. He knew to seek God in all things. But it remains somewhat surprising that when he died there was no one who had been trained to take his place as leader over our people.

Yes, our people knew that Jehovah God was our Leader. We knew we were His people. But for seventy years He had guided our people through the voices of men. Surely, He intended to continue that pattern! So, where was the man He had chosen to follow in Joshua's footsteps? Had Joshua not been listening to God? Or, had Joshua been disobedient to God by not mentoring the next leader? Or, did God have a much different plan?

When God required a leader to lead His people out of Egypt through the wilderness to His Promised Land, He knew where to find him. He went to a hillside and selected the shepherd He had prepared for the task. Then when He required someone to lead the people into the Promised Land to possess the land, He chose a man who had proven his military leadership capability time and again.

In both instances, God's selection and anointing were obvious. He raised up leaders with the unique gifts and ability for the assignments He gave them. But those assignments were now completed. His people were now in possession of the land. God no longer required one leader to lead all the tribes. Now each individual tribe needed to conquer the territory God had selected for them. And God had raised up tribal leaders through Joshua's leadership.

It soon became obvious God had a new plan for the governing of Israel.

Soon after Joshua's death, the Canaanite tribes began to stir. They believed our people were vulnerable to an attack because of his death and the absence of a successor. But Jehovah God had a different strategy.

He spoke to the hearts of the tribal leaders, and they asked Him, *"Which tribe should go first to attack the Canaanites?"*(1)

The Lord answered, *"Judah, for I have given them victory over the land."*(2) The leaders exercised wisdom, heeded the word of the Lord, and advanced according to the Lord's plan instead of going out on their own.

The army of the tribe of Judah was under the command of Caleb. By then, he was the oldest person living among our people, with all the wisdom derived from his faithful walk with the Lord. And even at 110 years of age, he still had the strength and courage of a younger man to effectively lead the fighting men of Judah. Caleb knew God would give them all they needed to faithfully accomplish His task.

His first action was to lead the tribe of Judah, the largest tribe of Israel, to enlist the support and cooperation of the tribe of Simeon, the smallest tribe of Israel. The tribe of Simeon possessed an allotment of land within the borders of Judah – in essence, the hole inside of the wheel. And it was mutually beneficial for the tribes to collaborate to conquer the remaining Canaanites living within their borders.

The two tribes defeated the Canaanites in the hill country cities of Bezek, Jerusalem, and Hebron. As they approached the city of Debir, Caleb vowed to give his daughter Achsah in marriage to the man who successfully led in the attack and capture of the city. The champion proved to be Caleb's nephew, Othniel, who was an honorable man.

Shortly after Othniel and Achsah married, she urged her new husband to ask her father for a field. But she soon realized the land in the Negev her father gave Othniel contained no springs of water. She knew the land would need a good water source to be productive and bear fruit. Othniel hesitated to go back to his father-in-law with an additional request. So, Achsah boldly went to her father and asked:

"Father, give me a further blessing," she said. *"You have been kind enough to give me land in the Negev, please give me springs as well."*[3]

Caleb, obviously concerned about his daughter's welfare and happiness, gave them not one spring but two.

I tell you this story for several reasons. First, as a daughter of Israel, I am a descendant of that union between Othniel and Achsah. Their great-great-granddaughter was given in marriage to the Benjaminite Ehud, from whom I am also descended. Jehovah God has blessed me with a heritage of faithfulness, passed down from the men and women who have walked before me.

Second, God has taught me through them that He will always provide the gifts, abilities, and resources needed to accomplish His purpose. Just as He provided leaders like Moses, Joshua, and Caleb, He will provide just what is needed, when it is needed, for whatever time it is needed. He has taught me to expect His provision, trust His provision, and look to His provision – whatever or whoever it happens to be.

Third, He has shown me through them that even though He is the same today as He was yesterday, I should not expect Him to always do things the exact same way. He will do what is appropriate for the hour in the way that is needed. His plan to conquer the land was different from His plan to possess the land. And His plan for us to inhabit the land today will look different as well.

Lastly, God has shown me through my ancestors that we all have a part in God's plan. Just like Moses, Joshua, Caleb, Othniel, and Achsah, He has uniquely made each of us to be a part of His purpose. No one is excluded.

God instituted a new era of leadership over our people – the era of the judges. That story begins with Othniel and Achsah … and, in many ways, so does my story.

~

2

OTHNIEL AND ACHSAH

Not long after Othniel and Achsah settled in the city of Debir, Caleb was laid to rest. Our people's zeal to conquer the land in obedience to the Lord died with Caleb. Instead, they turned their attention to settling the land, and the many years of fighting became a fleeting memory. Until then, God had allowed them to enjoy the fruits of the labor of those who had ruled before them. But now, they busied themselves with the task of cultivating the fields and planting the crops.

The men and women who had been born in the wilderness and had no memory of our people's enslavement in Egypt, now had children who had no memory of the challenges of the wilderness or conquering the land. They became complacent.

Settling the land took on many meanings – not all of which were good. God had given our people very specific instructions through Moses and Joshua before we ever set foot in the Promised Land:

"As for the towns of the nations the Lord your God is giving you as a special possession, destroy every living thing in them. You must completely destroy the Hittites, Amorites, Canaanites, Perizzites, Hivites, and Jebusites, just as the Lord your God has commanded you. This will prevent the people of the land from teaching you to imitate their detestable customs in the worship of their gods, which would cause you to sin deeply against the Lord your God."[1]

But our people failed to do as God commanded. Rather than driving out the people who occupied the towns, they settled in their midst. Over time, many of our sons intermarried with their daughters and many of our daughters with their sons. Many of our people began to worship their gods and forgot about the Lord our God. In short, most of our people did evil in the eyes of the Lord and abandoned His ways.

But Othniel and Achsah continued to honor the Lord God Jehovah. As the years passed, He blessed them with two sons, Hathath and Meonothai. From an early age, each boy revealed his own unique penchant. God gave Hathath the ability to tend the earth. He was able to cultivate barren fields and transform them into rich and plentiful gardens and groves. Each year's harvest exceeded the previous one, and the other residents of Debir could not fail to see the hand of God's blessing upon him. Soon, the surrounding fields also showed an increase as each neighbor began to follow Hathath's instruction.

Meonothai, on the other hand, was a skillful hunter. God gifted him with the trained eye and instincts of his grandfather Caleb, who had served Pharoah well as the master of the hunt in the days of Egyptian slavery. Meonothai also demonstrated the courage of his father and the shrewdness of his mother. He, too, became a recognized leader among the people of Debir and the surrounding cities.

Othniel proceeded to lead his family and the other residents of Debir to honor the Lord God Jehovah in all things. In turn, God blessed his family and the city with peace and prosperity, even as most of Israel did what was evil in the sight of the Lord.

Twenty years had passed since Joshua led the Israelites in his last major military campaign – the defeat of the northern kings. King Jabin of Hazor had rallied the northern kings to join their forces against the Israelites. It was a combined force of 300,000 foot soldiers, together with 10,000 fighting men on horseback, and another 20,000 in iron chariots.

They were much better equipped than the fighting men Joshua led. From a human perspective, the odds against our people were overwhelming. But the northern kings had failed to take into consideration one critical factor. The kings knew what God had done in defeating the enemies of Israel, but still they had refused to turn to Him. It wouldn't have mattered if the fighting force had been ten times that number – the Lord God Jehovah would go before His people and defeat those who had denied His Name.

God caused confusion among their warriors, and they fled in retreat. The Israelites chased them for two days – killing the warriors, crippling the horses, and burning the chariots. Our people found King Jabin hiding in the city of Hazor and executed him as God directed.

The day before our people arrived in the city, King Jabin sent his ten-year-old son away to safety. He was taken to the northernmost part of the Aramean kingdom, to the area called Aram-Nahrayn. There the boy was raised with hatred in his heart toward the God of Israel and His people. That boy grew up to become King Cushan of Aram-Nahrayn. He had matured into adulthood with the singular focus of seeking vengeance against our people.

Though the fighting force of Aram-Nahrayn had been rebuilt to 50,000 men over the twenty years that had passed, Cushan's councilors continued to remind him of how his father's much greater force had been defeated. Their fear of defeat kept the young king in check … at least for a time.

However, the king and his advisors were not aware of the Lord God Jehovah's anger over the wickedness of His people. Most of the Israelites had abandoned Him to serve Baal and the images of Ashtoreth, and they had forsaken the one true God. So, though King Cushan's military was not as mighty as his father's, they would not be fighting against the Lord God Jehovah. He would be leading his men to fight against the men of Israel without the protection of their God. And Jehovah God had already determined the outcome. He would hand His people over to the Aramean king.

3

A NORTHERN KING IS UNLEASHED

~

The cities of the smaller northern tribes of Asher, Naphtali, Zebulun, and Issachar fell quickly to King Cushan's initial advance. Word of the attacks spread among the Israelites but was met with confusion and despair. Our people were no longer organized as a fighting force. They had no leader because they had forsaken the One to whom they should have turned.

Their easy victories emboldened Cushan and his councilors to plunge farther south into the cities occupied by our other tribes. Each city fell with little opposition. Our disobedience was quickly causing us to lose all that God had graciously given us. But still, our people continued to turn to their false gods.

Within a matter of months, Cushan had occupied all the land except what was inhabited by the tribes of Judah and Simeon. Though he was able to advance into the most northern cities of Judah, he was unsuccessful in his attacks on Debir or the cities surrounding it. Jehovah God had looked upon the faithfulness of Othniel and his family and had protected them. Though Othniel, his sons, and the fighting men who joined them fought courageously and valiantly, they knew it was God who was truly keeping Cushan at bay.

Eventually King Cushan's advisors convinced him to be satisfied with his gains and not advance against the southern portion of Judah. They saw no reason to sustain further losses of their men. They reminded Cushan he had already conquered the cities of Ephraim, home to the descendants of Joshua, whom he blamed for the execution of his father, King Jabin.

So, Cushan turned his attention to the cities now under his control. He had no interest in making these cities part of his domain; rather, he planned to destroy them as retribution for what their fathers had done to his own father. He was determined to start with the cities of Ephraim. He began with Timnath-serah – the town Joshua had made his home.

Cushan's forces quickly identified Joshua's descendants – his grandsons and great-grandsons – and brought them before their king. He took great pleasure in torturing them before having them decapitated and their heads thrust onto long spikes positioned at the highest points of the town for all to see. Their wives and adult daughters were defiled and made to serve as slaves, while their children were taken away to Aram-Nahrayn to serve as slaves in the king's palace.

But that didn't quench Cushan's thirst for vengeance. He instructed his forces to torture and execute other tribal leaders in all the conquered towns and cities. The people throughout Israel were filled with fear and agony and began to refer to the king as Cushan-rishathaim – "the doubly wicked" Cushan. No one could remember another leader having been so evil. Truth be told, even the Arameans began to fear their king's lust for blood.

As the years passed, the Israelites continued in their spiritual blindness and cried out to their false gods for help – but none ever came. Finally, they remembered the God of their fathers – the Lord God Jehovah – and called out to Him for deliverance.

Throughout those same years, Othniel, his sons, and neighbors continued to hear reports of the havoc being wreaked upon the cities to the north. Although they had been successful in repulsing Cushan at their own gates, they feared their military would be insufficient to rescue their northern neighbors. As a result, they remained paralyzed by their fear and did nothing.

It was Achsah who called on Jehovah God throughout those years seeking His direction on what the people of Judah should do. The land of Israel had suffered at the hands of King Cushan for eight years when God finally spoke to Caleb's daughter.

She immediately went to her husband just as God had directed her and said, "Othniel, the Lord God Jehovah has said you are to go forth in His Spirit and lead His people out of their bondage. Just as He was with Moses, Joshua, and my father, He will be with you. He will go before you, and just as Joshua led our people to defeat King Jabin, you will lead our people to defeat his son, King Cushan."

Emboldened and empowered by the Spirit of God, Othniel sent out word to all the free cities of Judah and Simeon. "Brothers, the God of our fathers has promised He will deliver our brothers and sisters who are in bondage to the Arameans. We are to assemble and march on their cities and defeat their captors. Do not fear King Cushan-rishathaim because the Lord our God will go before us as our banner and our shield."

Over the next several days, the men assembled on the plain to the north of Debir to become a fighting force of 80,000 men. They did not have the weaponry, chariots, or cavalry of the Arameans – but they had something far more powerful. They had the Spirit of God going before them!

Throughout the years, Cushan and his forces had become complacent. They believed their reign of terror over the Israelites had made them incapable of rebellion. So, they were not expecting an attack when the army of

Judah and Simeon appeared at the gates of Jerusalem. The Aramean response was too little too late, and within moments the Israelites living in the city had been freed of their eight-year captivity.

From there, Othniel led the fighting men from city to city. Though the Arameans were now prepared for attack, their efforts made little difference. The God of Israel was always victorious, and His army marched with praises to Him on their lips. More men joined the fighting force from each city as they were freed, and soon their number exceeded a quarter of a million fighting men.

~

4

THE FIRST JUDGE IS RAISED UP OVER ISRAEL

Othniel's spies reported that King Cushan was assembling most of his fighting force around the city of Timnath-serah. He was determined to stand his ground there at the homeplace of Joshua. Othniel knew Cushan's forces had the advantage of higher ground, but he also knew he had the greater advantage – Jehovah God was going before His people.

The night before the planned attack, the Lord gave Othniel this promise: "Do not be afraid of King Cushan. By this time tomorrow, he and his army will be dead men. Then you must cripple their horses and burn any chariots that remain."

The Lord told Othniel he and his fighting men should not form ranks in Timnath-serah as Cushan would expect. Rather, they should follow the same instructions the Lord God gave Joshua when he defeated King Jabin. They were to immediately attack the enemy.

Othniel followed the Lord's instructions, and Cushan and his men were caught by surprise. Israel's fighting men were already upon them before they could mobilize their cavalry or their chariots to attack. Cushan and his commanders became so confused and disoriented their warriors began to flee.

However, Cushan refused to retreat. He went to the highest vantage point and shouted at his men to stand their ground and fight – but to no avail. The battle was lost, and his men bolted in droves. Our men pursued them and followed the Lord's instruction not to leave any man alive.

Unlike his father who hid in defeat, Cushan was enraged and shouted taunts at Othniel. "Let this battle be decided by the fate of the two of us!" he screamed. Both men knew Cushan was the younger of the two and had the physical advantage. But Othniel knew his trust was not in his own power but in the Spirit of the Lord.

The two warriors met at the gates of the city with swords in hand. Their one-on-one battle continued for more than an hour, and both men were physically spent. Cushan's strength came from his hatred; Othniel's from the Spirit of the Lord. Both men lost their footing several times during the match, but each time they were able to regain their position – until finally Othniel struck the blow that brought Cushan to his knees.

As Othniel looked into Cushan's eyes, all he saw was defiance. Cushan did not plead for mercy for himself or his men. There was no regret for his actions. He seethed with hatred directed not only at Othniel but more vehemently toward Jehovah God. His rage stamped such an indelible expression on his face that it remained even after Othniel's true blade severed Cushan's head from his body. As his body collapsed to the ground, the attempted retreat of the remaining Arameans who had continued to fight beside Cushan was immediately foiled.

Not only were the people of Timnath-serah set free that day, but so were all of the remaining people of Israel who lived in the other cities that had been conquered by the Arameans. There was little left of the Arameans once the fighting was done. They would not rise again to attempt vengeance upon God's people. News traveled quickly throughout the surrounding lands that the God of Israel had once again rescued His people and defeated His enemy.

Once the fighting was over, Othniel and his sons returned to their home in Debir. Jehovah God established Othniel as a judge over all of Israel to institute justice and the practice of His law among all the people. There was peace in the land for the next forty years.

One year before he was laid to rest with his ancestors, Othniel witnessed the birth of his great-great granddaughter, Ayala, through the line of his son, Meonothai. Eighteen years later, she would be given in marriage to a Benjamite living in the village of Ai. His name was Ehud, and he was the man God would raise up to be the second judge of Israel.

In the years following Othniel's death, the people of Israel again turned their hearts away from the Lord and did evil in His sight. During those years, a cunning king of Moab ascended to his throne and began to put a plan in place to conquer Israel. He craftily entered an alliance with the Amalekites, who inhabited the lands on the south side of the tribes of Israel, and the Ammonites, who inhabited those on the east side. Once that alliance was in place, the Lord permitted the Moabite king to take control over His rebellious people.

Unlike Cushan, King Eglon of Moab was not motivated by vengeance against Israel in retribution for past injuries; rather, for him it began over a territorial dispute. You will recall that the tribes of Reuben and Gad, together with half of the tribe of Manasseh, were allowed by God to settle on the east side of the Jordan River. You will also recall that it was God's intention that all His people settle in the Promised Land, but He had permitted their request to settle for less than His best.

A portion of the land given to the tribe of Gad by Moses had been seized when the Israelites defeated the Amorites. But the Moabites had always believed that portion of land belonged to them – and not the Amorites – and even less, the tribe of Gad.

For almost one hundred years the people of Moab had resented the confiscation of what they believed to be their land – until one day King Eglon resolved to do something about it.

~

5

A REBELLIOUS PEOPLE AND A DEFIANT KING

Jericho was the first city Jehovah God led our people to defeat when they entered the Promised Land. After He led the people to destroy the city, He invoked this curse:

"May the curse of the Lord fall on anyone who tries to rebuild the city of Jericho. At the cost of his firstborn son, he will lay its foundation. At the cost of his youngest son, he will set up its gates."[1]

The city remained in ruins from that day forward, even though our people eventually forgot the curse and, even worse, turned their backs on the God who had pronounced it. After conquering the cities of Israel, King Eglon decided to establish a summer palace in the region to reinforce his rule over the land. His palace would be built on top of the ruins of Jericho, placing his own mark and majesty over the land.

He chose Jericho for two reasons. First, the city was strategically located as a gateway between the lands of Moab, Amon, and Israel. But the second reason was of even greater importance to Eglon. When he learned why the

Israelites had not rebuilt the city, his decision to do so was intended to communicate his defiance of the God of Israel.

The Moabite king used Israelite slave labor to construct the palace; it took eight years to complete. When it was finished, the colonnaded structure eclipsed every other building in the region, and its comforts surpassed even those of Eglon's palace in Moab.

Unbeknownst to Eglon, God had seen his defiance and was already at work to bring about the destruction of that palace and the one who dared to place his throne within it. God's plan of destruction would include a Benjaminite by the name of Ehud.

While Othniel was still judge over Israel, he instituted a leadership structure whereby each tribe of Israel selected a judge. Othniel, in turn, delegated responsibility to each of the tribal judges to oversee the system of justice and practice of the law. Ehud's grandfather had served as the first tribal judge of Benjamin under Othniel.

When Othniel died, the tribes could not agree on a way to select one judge to preside over them all. Regrettably, none of them sought Jehovah God for His direction. Instead, they chose not to select one judge over them all. Each tribe, however, did continue the practice of being governed by its respective tribal judge. The mantle of that leadership passed from one generation to the next. When Ehud's grandfather died, Ehud's father, Gera, became the judge of Benjamin.

Gera, like the other judges who ruled when Eglon conquered the people, had turned away from God. The judges were now self-seeking, ineffective leaders who were the means by which King Eglon could impose his will. He tasked them with the gathering of an annual financial tribute from their respective tribes and presenting it to him. Once his summer palace was completed, he directed them to bring it to him there.

When Gera died, the mantle of leadership for the tribe of Benjamin passed to Ehud. Like his father, his heart had turned away from Jehovah God. However, the Lord led Ehud to marry Ayala, a righteous young woman who had never turned her heart away from the God of Israel. She had continued to seek Him with all her heart, just like her fathers before her.

Ayala continued to bear witness to her husband: "The same God who led our people out of the bondage of Egypt and delivered us from the wickedness of King Cushan is able to again deliver His people from the hands of King Eglon. All He seeks is for us to turn from our wicked ways and turn our hearts back to Him. He promises that if we seek Him, we will find Him. If we turn to Him with our whole hearts, He will turn His face toward us.

"Husband, our people will look to their leaders. If you don't repent and turn to Him, how will they ever do so?"

Before long, Ehud heeded those words and turned his heart to Jehovah God. The people of Benjamin began to see the change in his actions and his words. He tore down the altars he had erected to false gods and instead openly worshiped the Lord. Soon people began to follow his example and called out to God for forgiveness and deliverance. Word spread to the other tribes, and soon they, too, began to cry out to the Lord for help.

The time came when the annual tribute from the people was due to be delivered to King Eglon. Ehud and the other tribal judges came together to fast, pray, and seek the Lord in what He would have them do.

After three days, Ehud spoke to the other judges. "I believe the Lord has shown me we are to gather the tribute and deliver it to him as usual. We are to trust God that He will show us what we are to do after that."

By faith, the people of Israel did as Ehud had said. And Ehud did one other thing the Lord had shown him. He crafted a double-edged dagger that was eighteen inches long and placed it in a sheath strapped to his right thigh under his clothing.

~

6

A TRIBUTE THAT LED TO FREEDOM

~

Ehud was left-handed. The men and women of Ai had repeatedly reminded his parents when he was young, he wouldn't amount to much because of this trait. His father and mother had tried to retrain him to use his right hand, but they were unsuccessful. Despite this perceived handicap, he had grown into a very capable and accomplished young man.

Though no one had ever heard of a left-handed tribal judge, when the time came for him to assume the role for the tribe of Benjamin, there was no doubt he was the man for the task. Little did they know Jehovah God had uniquely equipped him for the task he would be called upon to carry out.

Each year, King Eglon demanded the Israelite tribes present a tribute greater than the year before. This year he had demanded twelve tons of silver (one from each tribe) and one ton of gold from the tribes combined. Twenty-eight ox-drawn carts were required to transport it. Ehud, together with the other tribal judges, set out on their journey to deliver the annual tax payment to Jericho.

Though much of Jericho was still in ruins, King Eglon's magnificent palace was located at the highest point of the city on a man-made plateau. It was no easy venture to lead the heavily laden ox carts to that point in the city. As Ehud and the others approached the palace, they passed the Moabite idols lining the pathway. As they arrived, they could see the king sitting on his throne in the center of a colonnaded portico that extended from the main building. It provided the setting for visitors and subjects to approach the king with great pomp and ceremony.

The ornate jeweled throne on which Eglon sat was twice the width of what one would expect. It had been crafted to accommodate the king's great girth. He was so fat his neck blended into his shoulders and his head appeared to straddle his body like a pebble on a boulder. It would have been comical if the king's actions and behavior had not been so repulsive.

He was surrounded by a multitude who seemed to comprise his royal court. Tables laden with great mounds of food of all kinds were stationed on every side. Ehud could not help but think of the people of Israel who were starving while this king gorged himself.

King Eglon's voice was shrill as he directed the men to unload the tribute into his treasury under the watchful eye of the palace guards. After our men completed their task, they were told they could leave. The journey down took much less time, and once the other judges and ox carts had departed the city, Ehud turned back toward the palace.

As he arrived at the portico, the guards advanced to protect their king. Ehud called out to Eglon, *"I have a secret message for you."*[(1)]

"What could an Israelite have to say to me that would be of any importance?" the king mockingly replied.

"I have a message for you from the God of Israel," Ehud declared.[(2)]

The crowd surrounding Eglon began to laugh and ridicule Ehud. But he stood his ground staring intently at the Moabite king. Eglon looked back at him, and slowly the smirk disappeared from his face.

The king rose to his feet with the assistance of two servants. "I will speak with this man in my royal chamber," he commanded. Guards accompanied their king as he made his way to his chamber then looked uncertain as to whether they should remain. As they helped him settle onto his throne, he waved his hand directing them to leave. After a few minutes, only Ehud and King Eglon remained in the room.

"What is this message you have for me from the God of Israel?" he demanded of the Israelite. As he asked the question, he attempted to again rise to his feet.

At that moment, Ehud reached with his left hand, pulled out the dagger strapped to his right thigh, and thrust it into the king's belly. The dagger went so deep that the handle disappeared beneath the king's fat. Ehud made no attempt to withdraw the blade. The king slumped back onto his throne, and his bowels emptied though the open wound. Eglon made no sound. His body shuddered … and then he died.

Ehud carefully closed and locked the doors leading into the royal chamber before making his way to the latrine and escaping through the sewage access. When the servants returned to check on their king, they found the doors to the chamber locked. The odor that assaulted their noses led them to believe the king was relieving himself, so they respectfully waited.

After a long delay, when the king had still not come out, they became concerned and got the key to unlock the doors. They discovered their king slumped dead on his throne. A cry immediately went out to find the Israelite. "He has murdered the king!" they shouted.

Ehud, however, had escaped the palace as the servants were waiting outside the chamber. He was now making his way speedily on the horse that had been left waiting for him. The other judges were already sounding a call to arms as they made their way back to their respective tribes. Ehud went directly to Ai, alerting the people of his village.

"*Follow me*!" he cried. "*The Lord has given you victory over Moab your enemy!*"(3)

The Israelites took control of the lands surrounding Jericho and the shallows of the Jordan River, preventing the Moabites from advancing. Ten thousand of the strongest and bravest Moabite warriors died. Not one escaped!

So it was that Israel was freed from Moabite captivity that day, and Ehud became the second judge over all of Israel.

~

7

AN OX GOAD

~

The land was at peace for eighty years, and then Ehud was laid to rest.

But the day soon returned when our people forgot the oppression of the Moabites and embraced evil once again as they worshiped false gods. Some even turned into thieves and bandits, menacing the roads, and making travel unsafe.

Without any regard for a righteous God, lawlessness reigned over the land. Brother turned against brother. Selfishness and covetousness became standards of the day. In many respects, I think it would have been better if the threat had come from foreign people – at least that would have given us a common enemy. Instead, we became our own enemy. Marauding bands sprang up from within our own tribes.

Due to distrust, villages became isolated from one another. We were no longer one people; we weren't even twelve tribes. We had become a people divided into hundreds of clans, all suspicious of one another. It didn't take long for our outside enemies to discover our vulnerability. The first to attack were the Philistines who occupied the land to the northwest of Judah.

Ehud's grandson, Anath, was now the judge of the people in the village of Ai. He continued to walk in the ways of his grandfather, as did most of those living in the village. Even though it was difficult to see the Spirit of God at work in most of Israel, Ai was an exception. Jehovah God continued to bless this village. Ai's people enjoyed plentiful harvests and the favor of God in everything they did. In some ways, Ai became a light on a hill in the midst of a very dark land.

Anath did not take those blessings for granted. He knew they were the result of God's faithfulness to them more than it was their faithfulness to Him. A story had passed from generation to generation about how our patriarch Abraham had built an altar to worship the Lord in the hill country between Bethel and Ai. Over 500 years earlier, God had promised Abraham He would give this land to Abraham's offspring – and our people were now enjoying the fruit of that promise.

Ehud had begun the practice of going to that place in the shadow of the oak trees each year and offering a sacrifice of thanksgiving to God. Anath had continued the practice, and the annual time was now approaching. Though Anath knew those hills were no longer a safe place to travel, he also knew he needed to continue to do so and trust God for protection.

When the day arrived, he and his oldest son, Shamgar, set out on the half-day's journey to the altar with an ox that would be offered as the sacrifice. Shamgar had become an accomplished herdsman and used his long pointed ox goad to drive the animal in the path before them.

The men arrived at the place at midday without incident. Together they repointed the stones of the altar, gathered wood, and made the needed preparations. Then they lit the fire and offered the sacrifice as a thanksgiving offering to Jehovah God.

As they were preparing to leave, first one arrow and then another passed within inches of their heads and struck a nearby tree. The two men immediately ducked for cover as more arrows quickly followed. Anath and Shamgar counted ten attackers and, based on their appearance, decided the men were a Philistine war party. The father and son were clearly at a disadvantage – all they had were their hunting knives, one bow, a few arrows, and Shamgar's ox goad.

Suddenly the Philistines charged them. Anath knew they were too close to use his bow and arrows, so he picked up a piece of wood to use as a club, and Shamgar reached for his goad. The two men fought valiantly. When the clash was over, all of the Philistines were dead. As Shamgar looked around for his father, he saw him lying on the ground with a fatal wound to the side of his head.

Shamgar's anguish was quickly replaced by overwhelming anger. He wanted vengeance and justice for what the Philistines had done. But first, he needed to take his father's body back to Ai for proper burial. He fabricated a stretcher and set out on the journey. It was almost nighttime when he finally arrived back at the village. His family and friends immediately set about burying Anath's body as the law of Moses required.

Shamgar mourned for seven days before he set out on his mission of revenge. During the weeks that followed, he showed no mercy as he killed 600 Philistines with his ox goad. Fear of him spread throughout Philistia and no other war parties assaulted Israel. Shamgar's mother finally convinced him to stop pursuing the Philistines. He did so in honor of her. But until the day he died, there wasn't a man in Philistia – or Israel – who didn't fear him. Ai became a very safe place to live.

I would like to say the people of Israel turned back to God under the leadership of a judge named Shamgar. But the simple truth is, they did not. Our people continued to do evil in the sight of the Lord … and nothing my grandfather, Shamgar, had done made any difference.

8

A BEE

~

From the time I was a young girl, I remember my father telling me stories of my ancestors – Caleb, Othniel, Ehud, and Shamgar. He told me how God had used these men to lead our people in the way they should go. My father taught me about their courage. And most importantly, he taught me about their faith in Jehovah God.

But truth be told, my mother's stories influenced me even more. She recounted the lesser-known accomplishments of Achsah and Ayala. She told me about the strength and courage Achsah learned from her father to always do right even when others do not. She taught me to have the boldness of Achsah and never be afraid to ask God to provide all He has promised. She explained how Achsah had been the one to convince her husband to lead the men of Judah against King Cushan.

She also explained how the Spirit of God had worked through Ayala to lead her husband to repent of his sinful ways and turn his heart to Jehovah God. God had used her to provoke the courage in Ehud to lead our people to defeat the Moabites.

And my mother taught me how God had used my great-grandmother to calm my grandfather's heart and bring peace to our village of Ai. God had used each of these women to ultimately lead our people to follow God.

"That's why your father and I named you Deborah," my mother told me. "As you know, we also use that word to describe the insect that some refer to as a 'bee.' In the Oral Torah, our people are often compared to a 'deborah' (or a bee). Just as the nature of the bee is to collect pollen and nectar for others, so it is that we toil as a people – not for our own benefit, but for the purpose of bringing pleasure to our Father in heaven.

"Just as a bee's sting is used to inflict pain on those who do not go in the right way, the honey it produces is used to bring sweetness to the lives of those who do.

"And just as bees swarm behind a queen bee, so too do our people follow behind those who teach them and guide them in the Lord's wisdom and strength.

"Your father and I have prayed since before you were born that you might be a deborah that God uses, as He did your ancestors, to guide our people in wisdom and in strength. But do not lose sight that a deborah is a lowly insect. Allow your name to remind you to always remain humble no matter how God might work through you in the days ahead!"

Though the people of Ai continued to follow the Lord, most of the surrounding villages had long since turned away from Him. When my grandfather was still alive, our neighbors knew not to provoke the people of our village – they remembered vividly what had happened to the Philistines. Even the surrounding nations remained at bay. But when word spread that my grandfather had died, everything slowly began to change.

My father, Oded, followed in his father's footsteps and led our village in the ways of the patriarchs. He led the people to defend against attacks and assaults from our surrounding neighbors, but he was not the feared fighter his father had been. He was actually a gentle man with a quiet spirit.

When I came of age, my parents gave their blessing for me to marry an Ephraimite man named Lappidoth. We had known one another since childhood, and our union had been expected for many years. Lappidoth was a kind and tender man, much like my father, and I knew it was God's will for me to become his wife. But Lappidoth and I both knew I would never be a demure wife who remained quietly in the shadows!

Over the years, the Spirit of God has spoken words of wisdom and truth through me. As I grew older, my father – at first secretly – began to seek my counsel on matters people brought before him as the judge of our village. But as time passed, he began to openly seek my wisdom. In fact, the villagers soon realized he was coming to me, and some began to appeal to me directly.

When the time came that my father could no longer serve as leader of the village, he was unclear on what to do. Since I was an only child, he had no son to step up and take his place. He initially considered naming Lappidoth as his successor. But the more he considered the choice, the more uncertain he became. One day he came to me and asked my opinion.

"Deborah, it will soon be time for me to relinquish my role as judge over this village and name my successor," he said. "I had hoped your husband might be prepared to step into that position, but I now know he is less capable than I have been. I prayed that God would raise up sons through your union who could one day do so, but He has chosen to favor you with daughters.

"Daughter, what do you believe the Lord would have me do?"

As I pondered his question, I already knew the answer. But I sensed the Spirit of the Lord telling me to remain silent on the issue. Instead, He led me to say, "Father, you must continue to ask Jehovah God to show you the one He has chosen to be the next judge over our village. He will make it clear to you. Be careful to listen for His answer … and when He does, you will know what to do."

~

9

A CANAANITE KING AND A SARDINIAN MERCENARY

Over 250 years had passed since God had used Joshua and Caleb to lead our people to conquer and destroy the northern kingdoms of Canaan. The city of Hazor had been captured and burned to the ground; its king, Jabin, had been killed. Every living thing in the city was destroyed – except for the king's son who was secretly extracted from the city just days earlier.

Twenty years later, that son, King Cushan, followed in his father's footsteps and was killed at the hands of Othniel. Again, God gave our people victory and the cities under the king's rule were destroyed. But his lineage lived on in the village of Harosheth-Goiim.

For over two hundred years the descendants of Jabin and Cushan awaited the day they would exact their revenge on the people of Israel. When Shamgar was judge over Ai, an heir to the throne of Jabin named Tirshi rose to rule over his people. He led them to return to the site of Hazor and rebuild it. Since most of our people were doing what was right in their own eyes, he met no opposition. Soon the rebuilt city was prospering, and the number of its inhabitants was increasing daily.

King Tirshi saw the division among our people and knew the day of retribution against us was drawing near. He was so certain that he even named his newborn son Jabin. The conquered would rise to become the conqueror. And if it didn't occur during Tirshi's rule, he was certain young Jabin would lead his people to victory over Israel.

But Jabin grew to be a man of slight stature and frame. He would not be the warrior on the battlefield that Cushan had been. Neither did he appear to have his patronym's cunning or ability to lead his people in such an undertaking without significant help.

Tirshi's plan took a turn when his physicians diagnosed him with a terminal illness. The king knew his son needed to be surrounded by trusted advisors if the Hazorite kingdom was to rule the region once again.

Tirshi asked his generals to find a suitable military leader for his son. The one they selected was a general named Sisera. He figuratively and literally stood head and shoulders above the rest – despite the fact he was an outsider.

Years earlier, a young man arrived in Hazor from the island of Sardinia seeking fame and fortune. His fighting skills and courage enabled him to succeed as a mercenary. He didn't much care who hired him if they paid the bounty he demanded. Tirshi's thirst for vengeance against the Israelites provided a showcase for Sisera to display his talents. Soon, he was training others how to fight. In short, the Hazorites needed a leader who wasn't afraid to fight, and Sisera needed a fight for which he would be well paid. It was a mutually beneficial alliance.

As time went by, Sisera rose in the ranks of the Hazorite army. When Tirshi needed a trusted general to come alongside his son and command the army, Sisera was the obvious choice. Sisera would be loyal to Jabin – as long as Jabin paid him handsomely.

Tirshi had fueled a hatred in his son's heart for our people since Jabin was a little boy. By the time Tirshi died, King Jabin had no doubt that his destiny was to lead his people to destroy their Israelite enemies.

Jabin placed all his resources at Sisera's disposal to build an unbeatable fighting force. Iron was mined and fabricated to manufacture 900 chariots. Sisera convinced Jabin he needed to import Giara horses, native to the island of Sardinia. Sisera contended their size and strength were best suited for the soldiers' needs so Jabin authorized the purchase of 2,000 horses.

Sisera continued to build and equip his fighting force. Though it would be smaller than the army defeated by Joshua, it would be better prepared. Sisera was convinced his well-trained and well-equipped force would easily conquer our divided people.

Unbeknownst to Sisera, his greatest advantage was that our God would not be going before us; rather, the Lord was prepared to turn us over to Jabin and Sisera. Our people's evil actions and attitudes were a stench in the nostrils of Jehovah God. Not only would He not protect us, but He would permit the Hazorite army to be the hand of retribution He would use to discipline us.

~

10

A NEW JUDGE IN AI

~

While my father was still the judge of Ai, Jabin sent out his forces under the command of Sisera to conquer the northern city of Dan. The Danites were ill-prepared for the assault, and the city came under the control of Sisera within hours. Soon the sacrifice altars to Jehovah God were pulled down and replaced by ones to Canaanite idols. Our people were even less capable of withstanding the religious invasion than they had been to defend against the military attack.

One by one the other northern cities fell to Sisera's forces at an accelerated pace. The early military victories emboldened Jabin's resolve to unleash his vengeance on all our cities. It was early in Sisera's campaign that my father came to me seeking advice on who should follow him as judge.

A few days after our initial conversation, my father returned to me. "Deborah, last night Jehovah God spoke to me through a dream," he announced. "I dreamt that the walls of the city were encircled by Sisera and his army. Our people were fighting against his advance, but it was obvious our gate would soon be overrun.

"I called out to my mighty men who surrounded me saying, 'Is there no one who will meet Sisera at the gate and defeat him?' I looked at one man after another, but each of them turned away from me. Until one person walked into our midst and declared, 'I will go! With God's strength, I will defeat Sisera and his army. Allow me to go!'

"Deborah, that person was you! You were dressed in the armor of a warrior, but you spoke with the resolve of a judge! And at that moment, I knew God was raising you up to be our champion. God was telling me you are to be the next judge over Ai! And if He has chosen you, who am I to say otherwise? The one I have been seeking has been standing right before me all the time!"

My father paused and waited for me to reply. There was no doubt in my heart or mind that God had been preparing me for this day. But even though I knew my father welcomed my counsel, I also knew he had never considered me as his replacement until that moment. And I also knew few people in our city would look favorably on a female judge. But I knew with that same certainty God had chosen me for this role, and He would make the way for me to step into the position.

My father called our people together. They were not surprised He was preparing to name his successor since everyone knew he had been searching for weeks. But they were shocked when he announced it was me. A woman had never been a judge in Ai – and to the best of everyone's recollection, there had never been a female judge in all of Israel.

My father explained how God had confirmed to him that I was His choice for the role. Then he began to remind them of ways they had already seen me demonstrate the ability to serve in that capacity.

He called to one of the men standing in front of him. "Elias, do you remember when you and Reuben came before me seeking judgment on your property dispute? Do you remember it was Deborah who spoke up and helped the two of you settle your differences? Did she not demonstrate her wisdom as a judge that day?

"And Jacob, when Asa's ox injured you, who was it that ultimately settled the argument between the two of you?"

"It was Deborah," Jacob hesitantly replied.

My father continued to ask similar questions to other men standing around him. Each time the men acknowledged how God had used me to help them settle their conflicts.

"I turned to Deborah in each of those matters," my father continued, "because I knew God had given her the needed wisdom. And each of you came to know that as well. Why would you now not welcome her to serve as your new judge?"

For a few minutes, the men and women surrounding my father looked down in silence. Finally, one man and then another raised their heads and said, "When the time comes, may God grant Deborah the wisdom to judge over us."

That time came sooner than I expected. Several weeks later, my father fell ill with a fever. Nothing seemed to help, and his condition worsened. One afternoon, he mustered all his strength and called me to kneel by his bedside. He reached out and placed his frail hand upon my head.

As he began to pray, his voice suddenly got stronger: "Hear me, Oh Lord God of Israel! You have blessed me above all men with a loving wife, a beautiful daughter, and dear family and friends. You have blessed me with this daughter, whom You have anointed with great wisdom. You have chosen her to follow me as the judge of Ai.

"Grant her the wisdom and courage to accomplish all that You set before her in the days ahead. Grant her husband, children, and the people of this city the ability to support her in the responsibility You have given her. Grant her the bravery she will need to turn back the enemy that advances on Your people. And grant her Your favor in defeating that enemy – not only that Ai is protected from siege but also that there is peace throughout Israel.

"Grant her the strength to rise up like the sun, and grant that her name is recorded in the history of our people as one of our great leaders – following in the footsteps of Joshua, Caleb, Othniel, and Ehud. And cause our people to follow her steadfastly as she leads them to follow You."

As he finished his prayer, my father took his last breath … with his hand still resting on my head.

11

A FATHER'S BETRAYAL

~

When my ancestors, Caleb and Othniel, defeated the Canaanites to conquer the cities in the hill country, they were assisted by the Kenites, descendants of Moses's brother-in-law, Hobab. When the fighting was over, the Kenites settled among the Amalekites near the town of Arad.

Over the years, the alliance between our people and theirs remained strong. Each time our people rose up against our oppressors under the leadership of Othniel, Ehud, and Shamgar, the Kenites stood with us shoulder to shoulder in battle. But in more recent days, the Kenites turned away from the God of Moses and Hobab. They worshiped the gods of the Amalekites, which caused the relationship between our two peoples to become one of military convenience and not one of kinship and shared faith.

When King Tirshi was rebuilding the Hazorite kingdom with an eye on conquering Israel, part of his plan was to build alliances with the clans living among us – including the Kenites. He reminded the clans that this land had once been their home while our people were still slaves in Egypt.

He rekindled a resentment against our people and encouraged the clans' support in helping him return the land to its rightful owners.

In truth, Tirshi had no intention of returning the land to its original owners. But the clans naively embraced his deception. Abdon, the clan leader of the Kenites, chose to join him as an ally. Abdon and Tirshi soon developed what appeared to be a friendship. Upon Tirshi's death, Jabin was quick to solidify that relationship between Abdon and himself.

When Jabin began to conquer the cities of Judah, he shrewdly left the town of Arad in the hands of the Kenites. Jabin and Sisera arrived at Arad's gates with great pomp and pageantry bearing spoils from their victories as gifts for Abdon. The Kenites welcomed them into the city as victorious allies. Abdon arranged for a feast in their honor that would last for seven days.

Abdon's eight sons were skilled hunters, and he instructed them to keep the tables fully stocked with a variety of fresh game. This was to be a feast unlike any other. While Abdon's sons were away hunting game, their wives were busy preparing and serving the food. As the week passed, one of Abdon's daughters-in-law, Jael, caught the eye of General Sisera. She was the wife of Abdon's youngest son, Heber.

Sisera was feared throughout the land even more than Jabin himself. Abdon knew a strong personal alliance with the general would be in his own best interest. So, when Abdon learned of Sisera's desire to sleep with the young woman, he saw it as an opportunity to strengthen that alliance and immediately granted his approval. Heber was still out of town, and Abdon instructed his daughter-in-law to say nothing to him.

It wasn't until two weeks after Jabin and Sisera left the city that Jael told Heber what had taken place. Heber flew into a rage at his father's betrayal. "Father, how could you permit such a thing to be done to my wife … and to me?" Heber demanded. "You have dishonored her, and you have dishonored me!"

"I had no choice," Abdon responded. "We must maintain our alliance with Jabin and Sisera at all costs. In the scope of protecting our clan, it was a small price to pay. You must realize that, my son, and move on. Sisera is gone. You and Jael are rid of him. Go on and live the rest of your lives and forget about it."

"How can we possibly forget about it, father?" Heber asked incredulously. "You have robbed us of that which only the two of us were to share – and without any regard for us!"

"Leave our father alone," Heber's brothers interrupted. "He chose to do what was right for our people. You should realize that and be grateful that nothing more was asked of you!"

Heber declared he could no longer be part of a family or clan that had such disregard for one of its members. He decided to take his wife and get as far away from his father and Arad as possible. He and Jael set out that very day on a journey heading north. After twelve days of travel, they came upon a grove of oak trees on a hill overlooking the town of Kedesh. Heber was pleased with what he saw. The ground was fertile, wild game appeared to be plentiful, and he was a far distance from his father. This would be the place he would pitch his tent and raise his family.

Several weeks later, Jael discovered she was pregnant. She quickly realized the baby had been conceived around the time Sisera had slept with her. She had no way of knowing whether Heber or Sisera was the father of her unborn child.

She kept the news from Heber as long as she could. Though her husband had been compassionate when he learned how Sisera had defiled her, their relationship had definitely changed. They had been robbed of the innocence of their intimacy. Though they still loved one another, their physical relationship had grown distant. She was afraid the news of her condition might drive them further apart.

Her decision to conceal the news only made it more difficult when the time came to finally tell Heber. His initial surprise at why Jael had waited so long to tell him quickly paled as he realized the timeframe of the child's conception.

"Am I the father?" Heber haltingly asked.

"I do not know for certain," Jael replied sadly.

A moment that should have been a joyous occasion for this young couple would forever be overshadowed by the primal lust of Sisera and the selfish ambition of her father-in-law.

When the little boy was born, Jael knew instantly which of the men was the father. She loved the little one regardless, but Heber could not bring himself to do so. He refused to give the baby a second look. That day, the child became a wall between Heber and Jael. Though they remained together, there was no longer any expression of love between them ... and sadness reigned over their home.

~

12

A NAPHTALITE WARRIOR

During his later years, my grandfather, Shamgar, instructed several young men who were his pupils and proteges. He had become a student of the words and actions of Moses. He saw how Moses had mentored a number of young men, not the least of whom was Joshua. Shamgar decided to do the same and raise up a generation of young men with hearts like Joshua and Caleb – to serve God bravely and humbly, and trust Him fully. He hoped and prayed God would one day use these students to turn hearts back to Him.

One of those young men was a Naphtalite named Barak, son of Abinoam. Barak first caught Shamgar's attention when he rallied the people of his city, Kedesh, to defend themselves against an attack by renegade Aramean warriors.

Years earlier, the Lord had designated Kedesh to be one of six cities of refuge throughout Israel when the land was apportioned to each tribe by Joshua. Those six cities were a portion of the forty-eight cities set aside for the Levites. Kedesh was situated in the midst of the region designated for the tribe of Naphtali. Early on, the city was primarily inhabited by Levites and Naphtalites.

The law of Moses requires anyone convicted of murder be put to death, so these refuge cities were established to provide a safe haven for people who accidentally killed someone. Once inside the city, the assailant would be protected from those attempting to avenge the victim's death. A panel of Levites would judge whether the death had occurred accidentally or not. As priests, the Levites were mediators between our people and God. As such, they were gifted to calmly arbitrate between the attacker and the victim's family, ensuring no further unnecessary bloodshed would occur.

If the Levite panel determined the death was accidental, the attacker could remain in the city of refuge until the death of the high priest in office at the time of the trial. At that time, the attacker could return to his own city without retribution. However, if the assailant left the haven before the death of the high priest, the avenger had the right to seek revenge and kill him.

In the years that followed, the kings of Aramea and Moab had chosen to respect the designation of the cities of refuge and not destroy them. So, the well-fortified city of Kedesh had remained relatively unchanged through the years.

That is, until a large group of Aramean marauders became intent on pillaging whatever treasures the city might possess. They had decided the peaceful city would not be able to defend itself against their attack. However, they underestimated the resolve of the people and failed to recognize the presence of one young man who would valiantly rally his people.

Barak was a skilled shepherd like his father before him. He had learned to stand courageously between his flocks and charging predators, armed only with his staff, his sword, and his knife. No predator had ever gotten the better of him, and his courage was well-known throughout the region.

Barak was also a proven leader. On numerous occasions, he had rallied the other shepherds to join him in facing widespread threats to their herds caused by droughts, fires, floods, and large-scale predator attacks. He became a well-respected voice – not only among the shepherds but also among all the men of the city.

When the band of Arameans threatened to attack, Barak immediately took charge and stationed men, skilled with bows and spears, at defensive stations on the city's walls. He led those who, like himself, were skilled with swords and clubs to strike their invaders. The Aramean warriors were caught off guard and swiftly retreated. Barak and his men pursued them, and only a few escaped death. Before the sun set, peace had been restored in the city.

That victory became legend throughout the land and yielded two significant results. First, it sent a clear message to other renegades that Kedesh was not easy prey and should best be avoided. Second, it made Shamgar aware of Barak right when he was assembling his small group of young leaders to mentor.

Soon after I was born, my grandfather summoned Barak to come to our city. He remained in Ai for fifteen years. My grandfather trained him and helped him further sharpen his skills as a warrior. My grandfather told me on more than one occasion that Barak was the most capable warrior in Israel, a leader of men, and one he would turn to if an enemy ever attempted to attack our people.

After my grandfather died, Barak remained in Ai for a short while, grieving the loss of his mentor and friend before returning to his home in Kedesh. It would be nineteen years before I would see him again.

~

13

A SUPPORTIVE HUSBAND

My earliest childhood memories include a young Ephraimite boy whose home was next door to mine. We were born the same year and were both our parents' only child. Our parents were not only neighbors but best friends. So, it was no surprise that Lappidoth and I quickly became best friends, too. We believed Jehovah God ordained us to become friends before we were even born.

I never had much in common with the little girls in my village, so I rarely played with them. My mother knew early on that I was definitely my father's daughter! I was more interested in engaging in debate, discovering truth, and settling disputes than I was in keeping a proper home.

Lappidoth and I were very different as well – but we complemented one another. He was gentle. I was somewhat brash – at least more than my mother told me little girls should be. He was cautious. I was daring. There wasn't anything I would not attempt or explore.

One day, Lappidoth and I were out exploring in the hills. I was charging ahead without paying enough attention to my surroundings. As we approached a cliff, I was taken in by the beauty around us and stepped too close to the edge. Suddenly, the ground beneath me gave way. If it weren't for Lappidoth grabbing my arm, I would have fallen to my death into the ravine below. From that day forward, I knew he would always keep a watchful eye on me, while I would always help him take the risks he needed to take.

As we grew older, Lappidoth was the one who analyzed the details surrounding anything we encountered, but I was the one who made the necessary decisions. He always knew more than I did about almost everything, but I could take that information and do something with it.

When we were children, we liked to collect fireflies together soon after the sunset. One day it occurred to me that I was like a bee, and he was like a firefly. He always wanted to make sure the light of truth shone in every situation. As a matter of fact, his name, Lappidoth, means "to shine."

As we became adolescents, I realized other boys in our city were intimidated by me. Physically, I had more strength and greater endurance than most of the young men. They all knew – as did most of the city – that my father would sometimes ask my opinion about a matter over which he was deliberating – whereas most of the boys my age were still idle daydreamers.

But I did not intimidate Lappidoth. He always encouraged me in my pursuits in his gentle way. And I came to rely upon his quiet strength. He was there to humbly support and champion me as I began to achieve greater success. At the same time, I admired his diligence and conscientiousness in everything he did.

Lappidoth clearly inherited his father's carpentry skills. There wasn't anything he couldn't build or do with his hands – and whatever it was, it always reflected the highest level of craftsmanship.

I'm not exactly sure when we knew we would marry, but our parents later confided to us that they had known since we were children. I wasn't in any hurry to get married, and Lappidoth patiently waited for me. I decided he could ask my father's permission to marry me on my twenty-first birthday. The date was set, our wedding feast was arranged, and six months later we were husband and wife.

As the years passed, God blessed us with two daughters. The oldest, Alya, has the nature of her father. Her name means "to go up" – to always take the high and honorable road. It describes her, and her father, perfectly. Our youngest daughter's name, Noya, means "beauty of God." Lappidoth says she is a reflection of me, and I must admit she has much of my nature.

Lappidoth always knew I would follow my father as the next judge of Ai. Truth be told, I was more in doubt than he was. I knew how difficult it would be for the people to accept a woman as judge. But Lappidoth repeatedly reminded me, "The people know you. They have seen you grow up. They know you are just as capable as your father, if not more so.

"Jehovah God has created you for this role. He has gifted you to carry out this responsibility with wisdom and courage. If you doubt your capability, you are actually doubting Jehovah God Himself! Trust Him to bring it about in His way and in His time."

I have come to realize there aren't many men with the strength, humility, and courage to support his wife the way Lappidoth has stood beside me. But God enabled me to marry an honorable man who is just such a husband. In many ways, he is the greatest gift God has given me to accomplish this task. And I know God has placed him beside me to grasp my arm if the ground beneath my feet begins to give way.

14

THE ENEMY IS TURNED AWAY AT AI

The day began much like any other day. Alya and Noya were now eight and four, respectively, and had become a great help to me with household chores. I was holding court six days a week for a few hours each morning. I chose to hear disputes beneath a palm tree in a garden on the edge of our city looking westward across the valley toward the city of Bethel.

The palm tree was now referred to as the Palm of Deborah. Usually there were already people waiting for me when I arrived. Often it was a dispute between two neighbors or a disagreement between family members. Jehovah God granted me the ability to settle the disputes and disagreements with wisdom and grace.

Some days the burden of being a judge felt like more than I could bear. God used Lappidoth and my daughters to encourage and refresh me from the heavy weight I felt. I knew they were part of God's provision to lighten my load, just as my mother and I had been a part of His provision for my father.

That particular day, as I was listening to a matter being presented, I noticed unusual movement off in the distance. I initially thought it was a herd of animals migrating through brush in the valley. But soon I realized it was a large group of men. They were advancing toward Ai with speed and purpose. I stopped the proceedings.

"Gentlemen, I must interrupt you! I see a large group of men advancing toward our city, and I do not believe they come in peace," I exclaimed. "One of you run into the heart of the city and sound the alarm, 'We are under attack!' Tell the men to meet me at the city gate!"

The messenger set out with haste while I and two of the other men walked a little closer so we could see the men from a better vantage point. I quickly recognized them as King Jabin's warriors. Though I was aware of General Sisera's attacks on other Israelite cities the past few years, he and his forces had left our region alone. I was told they had avoided the cities of our tribe because of a lingering fear of Shamgar and the fighting men he had trained. Apparently, that was no longer the case!

I instructed the two men with me to continue watching the warriors so they could keep me apprised; I ran to the city gate to organize our men. All the way back, I asked Jehovah God for His wisdom, strength, and favor against this enemy. Lappidoth and the other men were waiting for me when I arrived.

"The Hazorites are advancing on our city from the western valley," I began. "Seal the city gate! Archers, position yourselves on the walls and release your arrows once the enemy is within range. Lappidoth, divide our fighting men into two ranks. One rank will remain here under my command, the other will follow you out of the city to a position in the northern field out of view of the enemy.

"Once the Hazorites have positioned themselves outside of our western gate, you will circle behind them cutting off their retreat. After our archers have reduced their number, the men under my command and I will pour out of the city and attack them head on. They will not be expecting a frontal attack, so we will use surprise to our advantage. Jehovah God will grant us victory today!"

The Hazorites arrived at our gate when the sun was directly overhead. I looked at them from atop the city wall and was surprised at how small their fighting force was – and that they were attacking us from the front at that time of day. Clearly, they were confident we would not fight back. They found, however, that nothing could be further from the truth!

Soon after my men and I initiated our attack, the Hazorites began to retreat. Lappidoth and his men were there waiting for them. God had already made it clear to me we were to show the enemy no mercy. The Hazorites' boldness proved they not only didn't fear us – they did not fear the God of our ancestors.

The fighting was over by midafternoon. Only a handful of the enemy had escaped, and not one of the remaining 500 men who attacked us was alive. By God's grace, we had not suffered a single casualty! God had truly gone before us and utterly defeated our enemy.

I directed Lappidoth to lead a group of men to locate the bodies of the leaders of this assault against us. I wanted to know if General Sisera had led the effort. As I suspected, because of the foolhardiness of the attack, he was not numbered among them. Evidently, this group had been under the command of one of his lesser officers.

Later that night, I called our people to offer sacrifices of thanksgiving to God for His miraculous protection over us. We did so over the next three days – and as we did, we sang songs of praise to our Lord.

In the days that followed, Jehovah God made it clear He was directing me to step forward as a judge over all of Israel to lead our tribes to defeat

Jabin's army and free our cities from captivity. I was to follow the example of my ancestors, Othniel and Ehud, and restore peace in Israel. God promised He would go before me and grant us His favor.

I knew what I must now do.

~

15

A COMMANDER IS SUMMONED

Two men arrived at my home a week later – one was my husband. He was returning from the city of Kedesh where I had sent him with an important message that I could only entrust to him. He had successfully delivered my message convincing its recipient to respond quickly.

I had heeded the long-remembered words of my grandfather. I called upon his protégé, Barak, to come to the aid of his people. His wrinkles and graying hair reflected the nineteen years that had passed since I last saw him. But he still had the same vigor and vitality of the man I once knew.

"Deborah, judge of Ai, I am honored by the invitation you have extended to me," he said with a slight bow of his head. "Lappidoth told me how Jehovah God granted you a miraculous victory over the Hazorite warriors here in Ai. His hand of favor rests upon you as it did upon your grandfather. There is no question He has called you, not only to be the judge of Ai but to be judge over all of Israel. I am your servant, just as I was to your grandfather."

"You honor me when you compare me to my grandfather," I replied. "You were his faithful servant and the one he often told me we should call on if we ever needed someone to command an army. That hour has come, Barak!

"This is what the Lord, the God of Israel, commands you: 'Assemble ten thousand warriors from the tribes of Naphtali and Zebulun at Mount Tabor. I will lure Sisera, commander of Jabin's army, along with his chariots and warriors, to the Kishon River. There I will give you victory over him.'"[1]

Barak looked at me for a moment before answering, *"I will go, but only if you go with me!"*[2]

"Why do you make that request?" I asked.

"Because you are the one God has called to be judge over Israel," he answered. "The people must see you as their leader as they did Othniel, Ehud, and Shamgar."

"But it is Jehovah God who is their leader, just as it was in the days of Moses and Joshua," I corrected him. "The people must see Him and give Him all glory – not you and not me!

"Nonetheless, *I will go with you,* as you have requested. *But since you have made this choice, you will receive no honor. The Lord's victory over Sisera will be at the hands of a woman*[3] – but they will not be my hands. He will use the hands of another woman to bring honor and glory to His Name – and all the nations will know it is the God of Israel who has defeated His enemy.

"Let us make ready for the journey. We will depart at dawn. And Barak, we will take a short detour as we go."

The next morning, Lappidoth, Barak, and I headed out. God impressed upon me we needed to travel east to the Jordan River before we turned north toward the cities of the tribes of Zebulun and Naphtali.

Just before dusk, we arrived at the plain surrounding the ruins of what had once been the city of Jericho. In front of us was the overgrown rubble of what once were the impenetrable walls of the city. Even the palace King Eglon had subsequently built on top of the ruins had crumbled away.

As we stood there, I could hear the faint echo of people's taunts from the past as they hid behind the city's walls spewing hatred at the Israelite people below. They had underestimated the power of the one true God. They had dared believe their walls and their weaponry could defeat Him.

"It wasn't the might or ability of our people, Barak," I said. "It was the majesty and power of our Almighty God that defeated these people and erased them from this land. No man can take credit for what was done – not Joshua nor Ehud who came after him. Nothing could defeat our God then, and nothing can defeat Him now.

"We do not prepare to fight a battle in our own strength. It is not our muscles that must be fit and ready; rather, it is our hearts that must be inclined toward Him. And if they are, Sisera does not stand a chance!"

As we prepared to make camp for the night, I felt we were standing on holy ground. I knew we were on the Lord's journey. He was going before us. This was all unfolding according to His timing. I slept soundly knowing we were walking in the center of His purpose and His presence.

When the morning sun began to peek over the eastern horizon, we set out on the remainder of our journey. We knew we no longer needed to look at past victories of God; we knew His victory was ahead – victory that would also bring glory to His name.

In two days' time, we arrived in the cities of the tribe of Zebulun where we witnessed how God had gone before us … once again.

16

THE MARCH UP TO MOUNT TABOR

~

The small towns of the tribe of Zebulun had been conquered by Sisera over five years earlier. They were a shell of the towns and villages they had once been. Their young men and women had been taken captive as slaves and sent to Hazor to serve King Jabin. Their parents were left to mourn their loss and to eke out a meager living barely sufficient to pay the taxes Jabin demanded. Periodically, Sisera led his army through the region to ensure the people continued to live in fear.

Barak was better known to these people than I was. He was renowned for his prowess as a warrior and commander. So, it was Barak who introduced me when the people gathered in the first town to see who we were and why we were there.

"People of Kattath, the judges Othniel and Ehud are both well-known to you. God used those men to lead our people to overcome the oppression of our enemies and return us to a life of peace. Your ancestors followed in that pursuit and saw God grant them defeat over their enemies. The judge Shamgar is also known by you for his heroic victories over the Philistines – keeping them at bay from further aggression.

"You know I fought with Shamgar and considered him to be like a father to me. I now stand before you in the company of Shamgar's granddaughter, Deborah. She has followed in her grandfather's footsteps as the judge of Ai. She has his wisdom and courage. Just last month, she led the people of her city to defeat the forces of Sisera when they attempted to overtake Ai. Every one of those Hazorite warriors was destroyed – but not one of the warriors of Ai was killed. God granted them His great favor!"

I noticed the people began nervously looking at each other. The longer Barak spoke, the more anxious they became.

"God has called Deborah to lead us to defeat Jabin's forces and return our land to peace. Under God's direction, she has asked me to command an army of 10,000 warriors for that purpose, and we have come here to enlist your help. We need every man who is able to fight to join our ranks."

Instead of the resounding cheers we anticipated, the people began to grumble and tell us to leave. "Get out of here," one said. "We don't want you here," another added. "Jabin will have our sons and daughters slaughtered if he finds out we've even listened to you," a woman shouted. "Get away from us and leave this place!"

I had not expected this degree of fear. "We have cried out to God," another said in desperation, "but He will not listen."

"Jehovah God has listened to you!" I shouted. "He has heard your cries – and the cries of the people in the cities throughout this region. He has also heard the cries of your sons and daughters who are being held in captivity. And in response, He has said 'Enough!'

"God has sent Barak and me to tell you He will give you victory over Sisera. Just as God gave our people victory over their Aramean and Moabite oppressors, so shall He free us from these Hazorite tyrants. He will free us from our bondage so we will be free to follow Him and worship Him!

"Turn from the fear and desperation that overwhelms you, and turn back to the God who has time and again freed us from our oppressors. He is our God, and we are His people! Trust Him to lead us to victory and freedom! Join us in this cause that is just! Entrust your sons and daughters to Him, for He will protect them! Do not allow your fear to keep your sons and daughters in shackles any longer! Come with us and see the deliverance of Jehovah God!"

Suddenly, I saw the people's expressions begin to change. I do not believe it was the power of my words; instead, I believe it was the power of our God. They knew His promise was true, and His might was sure. They knew the time of His deliverance had come.

When we left Kattath a few hours later, seventy-five men marched with us. They were a small band of farmers – not warriors – but they were marching behind Jehovah God who was going before us as our banner!

Initially, we received a similar welcome from the towns of Nahalal and Shimron. But as I told them the promise that God had given us, and they saw the conviction of the men from Kattath, they too came around. Our numbers began to multiply as we visited town after town.

Soon, word of our coming outpaced our travels, and the cities and towns began to welcome us with open arms. I realized the victory God had promised was already happening. Our people were already being freed from their bondage. Their gazes were already turning back toward heaven!

We continued to the cities of the tribe of Naphtali. By the time we arrived in Barak's city of Kedesh, there were already 8,000 fighting men in our rank. Shouts of victory awaited us as we marched into Kedesh.

When the time arrived for us to march up to Mount Tabor, there were 10,000 fighting men in our company. We knew that word had already made its way to Sisera, and we knew he would not be far behind.

17

VICTORY IN THE PLAIN

~

When all was said and done, our fighting force was made up of men from the tribes of Ephraim, Benjamin, Issachar, Zebulun, Naphtali, and the western clans of Manasseh. They had joined in the fight for their common defense and protection. Some, like those of us from Ephraim, had suffered very little at the hands of Jabin but saw it as our duty to come alongside our brothers.

But, alas, not all our tribes had responded in kind. The tribes of Reuben, Gad, and the eastern clans of Manasseh were now settled on the eastern shore of the Jordan River and had completely disassociated themselves from the rest of us. The river was no longer simply a physical boundary, it had become the dividing wall Moses had feared it would become. The eastern tribes had no sense of obligation to come to the defense of their western brothers.

Over the years, the tribes of Asher and Dan – whose regions bordered the Mediterranean Sea – had forged trading relations with the Phoenicians and other Gentile nations, many of whom had alliances with the Canaanites. They feared their involvement in the fight against Jabin's army would sever those relations. Tragically, their desire to feather their nests with the twigs from the rest of the world was more important to them than standing by their brothers.

The tribes of Judah and Simeon considered themselves to be completely out of the fray. Jabin had shown no interest in attacking the cities that far south, so they refused to get involved despite my warning that he could be headed for them next.

We were told Sisera's army was now about 900 iron chariots, 10,000 horsemen, and 300,000 footmen. The bulk of his force was camped outside Harosheth-haggoyim, while the remainder was in Hazor with their king. My spies reported that Sisera and his forces would complete their twelve-mile march and arrive at the Kishon River at the base of Mount Tabor early the next morning.

Barak, Lappidoth, and I knew the odds were against us. Sisera's men were well-trained and well-equipped soldiers. They had been serving and training together for years. Our men were farmers, shepherds, carpenters, and merchants. We didn't have one chariot, let alone 900. We had only a handful of horses. And most of our men had never fought at all, let alone in battle. "Militarily speaking," Barak reminded me, "we don't stand a chance!"

Just then, from outside of my tent, we heard a handful of musicians begin to sing:

"When Israel's leaders take charge,
and the people gladly follow –
bless the Lord!

Listen, you kings!
Pay attention, you mighty rulers!
For I will sing to the Lord.
I will lift up my song to the Lord, the God of Israel.

The mountains quaked at the coming of the Lord.
Even Mount Sinai shook in the presence of the Lord, the God of Israel.

You who ride on fine donkeys
and sit on fancy saddle blankets, listen!
And you who must walk
along the road, listen!

Wake up, Deborah, wake up!
Wake up, wake up, and sing a song!
Arise, Barak!
Lead your captives away, O son of Abinoam!

Lord, may those who love You rise like the sun at full strength!
And may all Your enemies die as Sisera will die!"[1]

I turned to Barak and said, "No, it is Sisera and his warriors who do not stand a chance! Our God fights for us! Let us rise with the sun at full strength and follow Him into victory!"

At sunrise, Barak led our warriors as they charged down the slope of Mount Tabor into the midst of Sisera's forces on the plain beside the Kishon River. They were not expecting us to attack. God used our sudden arrival, together with the chaotic shouts of our warriors, to disorient the Hazorite army. Sisera, his charioteers, his horsemen, and his footmen all panicked.

They trampled over one another as they ran in retreat. Our warriors followed in pursuit the entire twelve miles back to their camp in Harosheth-haggoyim. The fields were soaked with Hazorite blood. And by the time the fighting was over, not a single Hazorite warrior was left alive.

By God's mercy and grace only a handful of our warriors died that day, and a surprisingly small number were wounded. God had given us a miraculous victory – one to be remembered for time and eternity.

As I stood there overwhelmed by what Jehovah God had done, Barak came to me with a report. "Sisera has escaped! He leapt down from his chariot in the heat of the battle and ran away on foot. Several of our men tried to follow him but got caught up in the fighting. He has disappeared. Our men are combing the land between Mt. Tabor and Harosheth-haggoyim, but so far without success.

At first, I could not hide my disappointment. How could we have possibly allowed this man to escape? Why had we not taken greater care to make sure he, of all people, was brought to justice for his crimes? As a judge, I had seen men put to death for much lesser crimes than this man had committed.

But then I remembered God's promise: *"The Lord's victory over Sisera will be at the hands of a woman."*[2] And I knew I was not that woman.

I sensed the Spirit of the Lord as He said to me, "Watch and see the victory of the Lord!"

~

18

A GENERAL'S ESCAPE

~

Sisera made his way on foot back to Harosheth-haggoyim just ahead of his retreating army. Apparently, he mistakenly thought our warriors would not pursue his men all the way back to their camp. He planned to rally his forces and lead them back in a coordinated attack to reengage us. But when he saw that most of his army was not going to make it back to camp, he realized the day was lost.

He had a reputation of dressing in a most ostentatious manner – even in battle. Sisera never wanted anyone to be unaware that he was the infamous general of the Hazorite army. Over the years, he had continually added epaulets and medals to his uniform, boasting of his superiority over everyone – except possibly his king.

But now that he knew our forces would be hunting him down, he no longer wanted to call attention to himself. He quickly cast aside all his frills and finery and dressed like a common farmer.

Barak and I were certain he would attempt to make his way to Hazor to reunite with his king and the remaining portion of his army stationed there. Hazor is about thirty miles northeast of Harosheth-haggoyim with a lot of open land between the two cities where someone could easily disappear. Our men began a careful search for him in that direction.

We later learned he had traveled southeast, away from Hazor, toward the town of Beit She'an along the Jordan River. Beit She'an is an Egyptian stronghold in the region. It would appear Sisera was planning to enlist the aid of the Egyptians in defeating our forces and solidifying Hazorite control over our cities once and for all.

The Egyptian administration of Beit She'an had good reason for wanting to hear his proposal. You will recall that King Thutmose II was pharaoh of Egypt when Moses led our people out of bondage. He had led his army to pursue our people with the intent of bringing them back to Egypt. But his effort resulted in his own death when God released the waters to close the dry path through the Red Sea. His son, Thutmose III, became the next pharaoh of Egypt during the time our people were wandering in the wilderness.

Thutmose III was determined to rebuild the Egyptian empire into what it had been before his father led it into ruin. He went about reestablishing control of several regions to the east of Egypt. While Moses was still leading our people through the wilderness, Egyptian forces under Thutmose III's command were victorious over a coalition of Canaanite vassal states in what was called the Battle of Megiddo. Beit She'an became the center of governance over the region they conquered. To this day, they maintained a strong presence in the city.

The Egyptians and our people had remained at peace ever since God had led us into the Promised Land. Thutmose III and the pharaohs who followed him had a healthy fear and respect for the Lord God Jehovah and had no interest in again inciting His wrath. We had stayed clear of one another for the almost 300 years we had been in this land.

But we came to learn that Sisera intended to open those old wounds and convince the Egyptians to extract their long overdue revenge against us. Apparently, the Egyptian leaders weren't opposed to the idea, because Sisera ended up spending several days in Beit She'an discussing a plan with them.

We will never truly know the outcome of his visit, but Barak and I came to believe that Sisera departed the city with a proposal to present to King Jabin. He traveled north along the western shore of the Jordan River on what should have been a two-day journey to Hazor. Evidently, he was convinced his king would overlook his humiliating defeat once he learned of the strategic alliance he had negotiated with the Egyptians.

Sisera was apparently aware that Heber the Kenite had pitched his tent in the grove of oak trees overlooking Kedesh almost two years earlier. He also knew the site was almost halfway between Beit She'an and Hazor. It would provide a comfortable place for him to rest overnight before completing his journey. Sisera remembered the overwhelming hospitality Heber's family had extended to him and King Jabin during their last visit in Arad. He had no reason to believe their welcome would be any less hospitable this time.

I'm certain he believed this would be a safe place to rest and finalize his thoughts on how to best present his grand proposal to King Jabin. He would have also remembered that Heber's wife had been given to him for the night the last time he had seen them. He would have had no reason to believe this time would be any different and he would have relished the thought.

As Sisera approached the hill overlooking Kedesh, he saw the familiar signs of a Kenite encampment in the distance. The familiar blue banners were billowing in the breeze. A handful of animals were visible in an enclosed area beside the main tent. A portion of the land had obviously been cultivated and seeded in preparation for what would soon be a bountiful harvest. Everything appeared to be at peace.

The only sign someone was in the camp was the plume of smoke gently escaping from a cooking fire on the other side of the tent. He probably believed he had outsmarted us by taking a circuitous route, but still he remained cautious. He slowly approached the camp, scanning carefully for lookouts.

Suddenly, a familiar figure stepped out of the tent. She looked the same as when he last saw her. At first, her attention was turned in another direction, but as he continued to walk toward her, she looked up. Her expression confirmed she knew who he was.

19

AN UNEXPECTED VISITOR

~

Jael could not believe her eyes. The one who was the cause of all her pain was back. Night after night, her dreams were haunted by how this man had defiled her and how her father-in-law had betrayed her. When she and Heber moved to this place, she thought she had left that pain behind them; but that was not the case. The pain had followed them – and in some ways, had gotten worse.

But she certainly never expected to see Sisera again. Yet, here he was on her doorstep with Heber away from camp leaving her unprotected again. Her husband was gone most of the time now, and she did not expect him back for several days.

Since that fateful night almost two years earlier, Heber seemed to blame her for what happened. He rarely spoke to her, and he would not even look at their one-year-old son. As a matter of fact, he never referred to him as their son – only as *her* son.

But Jael knew none of this was her fault. She had been left to fend for herself by her husband – though she knew he could not have known what would unfold that night. But his treatment of her since then had been unforgivable. And now the one she blamed the most – the one who had not shown any signs of remorse for his actions – was walking toward her. He had ruined her life so he might have one night of pleasure.

Throughout every one of her sleepless nights since then, Jael had called out to Jehovah God for someone to avenge the evil that was committed against her. Repeatedly the Lord reminded her of His promise from the Song of Moses:

"I will take vengeance; I will repay those who deserve it.
In due time their feet will slip.
Their day of disaster will arrive,
and their destiny will overtake them."[1]

And she knew her God would be faithful. He alone could take that which was intended for evil and use it for good. In fact, that is why she had chosen to name her son Joseph. The favored son of Jacob had stood tall amid the evil that had been carried out against him by his own family, and she was confident the same would be true for her son.

As Sisera drew closer, an avalanche of emotions welled up inside her. The anger she felt toward him was suddenly overshadowed by fear. He had already demonstrated she was no match for him physically. He had been able to have his way with her despite her efforts to thwart his advances. She knew he was a man without morals who did not fear God. She was afraid for herself but even more so for her son who was fast asleep in the tent. She feared not only for his safety but also that nothing would happen to traumatize him.

She quickly decided her goal was for Sisera to leave her home as soon as possible with as little danger to her and her son as possible. She silently – but fervently – asked God what He would have her do.

The first words out of Sisera's mouth when he reached her were: "Jael, you look as lovely as when I last saw you! Is your husband here as well, or are we to be alone again tonight?"

He made no attempt to hide his intentions. After he made sure they were indeed alone, he asked what she was preparing on the cooking fire. "I am quite famished, and I have been looking forward to a good meal prepared by your delicate hands," he said.

Sisera entered Jael's tent as he spoke. Immediately he saw Joseph sleeping in the cradle on the other side of the tent. "I see you and your husband have been blessed since I was last with you," he said without any thought or concern that the child might be his. "I hope he is a good sleeper, because I have no tolerance for crying babies!"

By God's grace, Joseph did remain asleep for the remainder of that day and throughout the night. As a result, Sisera never gave the sleeping child another thought. Jael went about the work of preparing a meal for Sisera.

While Sisera dined, he began to confide to Jael about the defeat of his army at Mt. Tabor. "It was a minor setback," he lied. But he went on to assure her that he had a plan by which the Hazorites would ultimately prevail. "All I must do is avoid the Israelites who are after me and get to Hazor by tomorrow night," he added.

After he had eaten his fill, he made his intentions clear. Jael was faced with the decision of placing her son in danger or succumbing to his demands. She chose the latter, but she now knew she would be able to use Sisera's anxiety about the Israelites pursuing him to her advantage.

"Come into my tent, sir," she said. *"Come in. Don't be afraid."*[2]

God graciously gave her the strength to endure his physical advances until he had completely exhausted himself. When he no longer had the strength to continue, she covered him with a blanket.

"Please give me some water," he said. *"I'm thirsty."*[3]

Jael gave him milk instead to help him sleep more soundly and covered him with another blanket, so he was good and warm.

"Stand at the door of the tent," he told her. *"If anybody comes and asks you if there is anyone here, say no."*[4]

"I will make sure no one else comes into the tent, sir," Jael replied. "Sleep soundly and rest well."

~

20

AT THE HANDS OF A WOMAN

~

As Jael stood at the entry of the tent, she could see by the light of the moon that Sisera was sleeping soundly. She began to formulate a plan as she watched his chest rise and fall with each breath.

At first, her plan had been to passively submit to his demands so no harm would come to her or Joseph – and then Sisera would be on his way the next morning. But as she watched him sleep, she realized he must be held accountable for his evil actions – against her and so many others. She wondered whether she was being given the opportunity to mete out justice for all his victims.

Her eyes searched the tent for a weapon. Jael saw the bow and arrows Heber had left for her. But she feared what would happen if her aim was off and the arrow missed its mark. Sisera would wake up in a rage, and she and her son would be killed.

She then considered Sisera's sword lying beside him. But she was afraid the sound as she withdrew it from its sheath would awaken him. She was beginning to lose her nerve. Perhaps she should just let her original plan unfold and leave Sisera's punishment to the Israelites.

Then Jael spotted a hammer and tent peg near the inside edge of the tent where Heber had left them. Sisera was sleeping with one side of his head resting on the ground. With one solid blow on the tent peg, Jael could force it through the soft temple on the side of his skull. He would die instantly. But unlike using the bow and arrow, she would have to kneel right next to him to complete the task. What if he awoke just as she was getting into position?

As fear began to grip her, she decided it was too great a risk. But just then, Joseph let out a soft cry. Her mind began to race. What would Sisera do if the baby woke him up? Would he kill her and her son? This was her moment. She had to take the risk to put this to an end once and for all!

Jael swiftly and quietly walked over and picked up the hammer and tent peg. Joseph did not make another sound as she silently crept beside Sisera. In a single motion, she placed the point of the tent peg just above his temple with her left hand and raised the hammer with her right hand. She took a deep breath and held it. Sisera made the slightest of movements, and she knew if she didn't strike now all would be lost!

The metal of the hammer meeting the head of the metal peg shattered the silence in the tent. It was followed by the sound of flesh and bone collapsing as the peg pierced Sisera's skull. His eyes flew open, and his body shook convulsively. Jael thought he was preparing to lunge toward her but realized the peg had gone all the way through his skull and he was now pinned to the ground.

She watched, frozen in fear, as Sisera gasped his last breath. Then just as suddenly as his body had started to convulse, it stopped. Blood began to pool under his head, and his face and mouth twisted into an expression of overwhelming pain.

Jael rolled onto her back and released the breath she had been holding. She lay there for what seemed like an eternity; it was as if time itself had stopped. The sun was just beginning to creep over the horizon when Joseph let out a quiet cry. It was finally over! Sisera's punishment had been delivered. Justice had been carried out – for her and all his other victims.

After covering Sisera with blankets, she began to wash away the spatters of blood from her face, arms, and hands. By then, Joseph was fully awake and made it clear he was ready to eat. As Jael looked down into her son's beautiful eyes, she knew he was the best thing his father had ever done – and now only the best of Sisera would live on.

After breakfast, Jael kept Joseph outside so they could enjoy the warmth of the sunshine and the beauty of the day. As she looked out over the horizon, she saw a small group of men walking toward her. She began to fear they might be some of Sisera's men looking for him. She knew what they would do if they discovered Sisera's body. She thought about fleeing, but she knew they had already seen her, and she could not outrun them.

She started walking toward the men and away from the tent. Perhaps she could redirect them, and they would never discover Sisera's body. As she walked, she turned her head heavenward and asked God what He would have her do.

~

21

MAY SHE BE BLESSED ABOVE ALL WOMEN

~

"My name is Barak," one of the men said as Jael approached the group. "I am the commander of the Israelite army. We are searching for the commander of the Hazorite army, whom we have defeated and destroyed at the Kishon River. Have you seen a solitary man making his way across this hill?"

"Why do you seek him?" she asked.

"So he can be brought to justice for the evil he has done against our people," Barak replied.

"In that case, I know where you can find him," Jael responded. "*Come, and I will show you the man you are looking for.*"[1]

Barak and his men followed Jael cautiously to the entrance of her tent.

"The one you seek, the one named Sisera, is inside my tent," she announced.

Barak and his men drew their weapons in preparation to do battle with Sisera until Jael exclaimed, "Put away your weapons! You do not need them. He can do you no harm."

Jael and her son waited outside as the men entered her tent. "You will find him lying underneath those blankets," she instructed them.

Neither Barak nor his men were prepared for what they saw.

Barak turned to look at the woman in disbelief. "Who has done this?" he asked.

"By God's strength, I did," she replied.

"But how were you able to overpower him?" Barak asked.

"Only by the grace of Jehovah God," she answered.

Barak thought about her answer before he responded. "Deborah – the judge over Israel – told me the Lord's victory over Sisera would come at the hands of a woman. And today, it has come to pass! Tell me your name so our judge and all the people of Israel can celebrate your victory over our enemy."

Jael replied, "Tell Deborah I am one who is a servant of the Lord God Jehovah. I am the mother of this precious little boy who is the best of his father. I am the wife of Heber the Kenite. And today the Lord has blessed me above all women who live in tents. My name is Jael."

She remained outside the tent with Joseph while Barak and his men wrapped and carried away Sisera's body. Before he left, Barak told her I would want to meet her and pay her tribute. Her reply surprised him: "God has already honored me in ways you will never know. He has permitted me to know Him as my Righteous Judge, my Protector, and my Strength. I do not require any further honor."

Later that day, Heber returned home. When he entered the tent, he saw Jael cleaning the blood stain from the floor. "What happened here?" he asked in shock.

"Today God has delivered us from our enemy," Jael replied. She then told him everything that had taken place.

Heber listened in horror at what his wife had been forced to endure yet again. He was overcome with sorrow as he realized his wife and child were vulnerable to such an attack because he had abandoned them. Sorrow turned to repentance as he grasped what his selfishness had nearly cost them all. And repentance turned to a broken and contrite heart as he sought his wife's forgiveness for his abandonment emotionally and physically.

All of that ultimately led to an overflowing admiration for his wife. Jael had done what he had failed to do. She courageously sought justice when he had selfishly run away. She had shown a strength of character that neither he nor his father possessed – and had remained steadfast despite the atrocities committed against her.

That morning, God gave her victory over an enemy and set free that portion of her life. Now, God was giving Heber and Jael victory over the forces that had worked to drive them apart as husband and wife. God blessed all of Israel that day – He restored us as a nation. But He also blessed that Kenite couple that day – He restored them as a family. The nation's restoration had taken place at the point of a tent peg. The couple's restoration had taken place in the shadow of shed blood, and that evening Heber sacrificed one of their lambs to Jehovah God as an offering of thanksgiving.

Barak and those traveling with him returned to our encampment that evening with the body of Sisera. We celebrated the defeat of our enemy and gave praise to Jehovah God. We knew, however, our victory was not yet complete. We planned to lead our forces the next morning to march on King Jabin and his remaining army in Hazor. Once he was defeated, we would truly be free of his captivity.

It would be several weeks before I was able to visit Jael in person and hear her story. I walk in awe of this woman who endured so much and yet walked in the strength and courage that – by her own admission – came solely from Jehovah God. I may be God's judge of Israel, and Barak may be His commander of Israel's army, but Jael is God's champion. She is truly *a woman blessed above all women who live in tents!*[(2)]

~

22

PEACE RETURNS TO THE LAND

~

Two days later, we were camped outside the city of Hazor. Our ranks had grown as word spread among our people about God's overwhelming victory at the Kishon River and the death of General Sisera. But the news had also made its way to King Jabin and the citizens of Hazor. Though the number of Jabin's fighting force was still greater than ours, fear was overtaking his heart and the hearts of his people.

He remembered, all too well, how the city of Hazor had been destroyed during the reign of the king whose name he bore. The God of Israel had fought for His people those many years ago just as He had on the day Sisera was defeated. Jabin's army under Sisera's command had outnumbered the untrained Israelite warriors – but their superior numbers had made no difference. The Israelites were victorious because their God was on their side. Jabin had never known fear as king until that day.

To make matters worse, Jabin had relied solely on Sisera to plan and execute their military strategies. Jabin had absolutely no ability in that regard and had little faith in the military commanders who now surrounded him. Sisera had left his least competent commanders behind in Hazor. He had wanted his best with him and never allowed for the possibility he might be defeated.

The king's greatest weapons throughout his reign had been the faithlessness of our people toward our God and our fear of Sisera and his army. In a matter of days, Jabin had seen both of those weapons destroyed – our people had once again been reunited with our God and now feared no one except Him.

That change was also obvious in the atmosphere around our camp. Just days earlier, only a few musicians were sitting around the fires singing, but now most of our warriors were joining in:

"Listen, you kings!
Pay attention, you mighty rulers!
For I will sing to the Lord.
I will lift up my song to the Lord, the God of Israel.

The stars fought from heaven.
The stars in their orbits fought against Sisera.
The Kishon River swept them away.
March on, my soul, with courage.

Lord, may all Your enemies die as Sisera did!
But may those who love You rise like the sun at full strength!"[(1)]

The next morning as the sun rose, Barak assembled our fighting men to attack the city. I stood on the rise just above them and called out, "This is what the Lord, the God of Israel has said, 'Get ready! Watch and see the salvation of the Lord. Today I have gone before you and vanquished your enemy! Today I have again given you this city!'"

Barak led the charge; I kept a watchful eye as we advanced on the city. We fully expected archers stationed along the top of their walls to greet us with a barrage of arrows – but none came! When the city gate opened, we waited expectantly for a full complement of trained horsemen wielding swords and spears to assault us – but none came! As we passed through the gate, we were prepared for a host of foot soldiers to charge us – but not one advanced on us!

Instead, what we witnessed shocked us – we were surrounded by a sea of death. Soldiers' faces were etched with terror, and it appeared they had turned on one another. The city streets and grounds were filled with blood and the smell of death. The shouts of our charge subsided as the last of our ranks entered the city in complete silence.

I directed Barak to come with me and bring a contingent of men as we made our way to Jabin's palace. When we arrived, there were no guards at the palace doors. Inside, there was no one to prevent us from entering Jabin's throne room. The only thing surrounding us was the same scene we had seen throughout the city.

Barak and I noticed Jabin seated on his throne at the same time. "He has the same expression of terror on his face I saw on Sisera's," Barak said. "But instead of a tent peg through his skull, he has a dagger thrust through his heart – and it appears to have been delivered by his own hand!"

Nothing could ever have prepared us for what we saw that day. We had witnessed great death at the Kishon River, but not like this. Our army never raised a sword or a spear. Our men never cast one blow. We did not lose a single life among our ranks that day. There was no mistake about Who had defeated the Hazorites!

I directed Barak to have our men leave the city and not take anything with them. They were not permitted to take any bounty. This was not our victory. We were not to profit in any way.

Once the men were safely outside the city walls, Barak instructed a few of them to burn the city to the ground; nothing was to remain. God had erased the Hazorites from the face of the earth. It was only by His mercy and grace that it was not us. Our disobedience merited that same punishment. And yet, God had remembered His covenant with His people. Not because we deserved it, but because of who He is!

As we watched the city burn, I knew we were standing on holy ground. In later years, when people spoke of the victories of Deborah and Barak, I immediately stopped them. There is only one name that can be attributed to the events that led to our freedom from captivity ... and that name is Jehovah God.

Peace had now returned to our land.

~

23

RELEARNING HOW TO LIVE IN OBEDIENCE

~

Our people knew how to live in disobedience to the Lord, but they needed to relearn what obedience looked like. They also had become used to living as a conquered people, but now they needed to be retaught how to live as a free people. You might think that should come naturally for them – but it did not!

The oppression under Jabin had lasted twenty years and our people had turned away from God long before that – so there was an entire generation that had never known anything different. And those who had, had long since forgotten. I knew that leading our people into battle to overthrow their oppressor would be less difficult than what I now faced.

I summoned all the tribal elders, leaders, and judges of the tribes that had joined us in battle to meet me in Shiloh, where the Lord's tabernacle and the Ark of the Covenant had remained since they were placed there by Joshua and Phinehas, the high priest. Uzzi, son of Bukki, was now the high priest. He and his fellow members of the Kohathite clan, which descended from Aaron, Eleazar, and Phinehas, had originally been charged by the Lord with the responsibility of caring for the Ark and the vessels of worship. In previous decades, the tabernacle had fallen to ruin and our people had abandoned their worship of Jehovah God. It was now time for the sons of Kohath to lead us by carrying out their responsibilities.

Once everyone had arrived in Shiloh, I stood before them and read from the Song of Moses:

"Listen, O heavens, and I will speak!
Hear, O earth, the words that I say!
Let my teaching fall on you like rain;
let my speech settle like dew.

Let my words fall like rain on tender grass,
like gentle showers on young plants.
I will proclaim the name of the Lord;
how glorious is our God!

He is the Rock; His deeds are perfect.
Everything He does is just and fair.
He is a faithful God who does no wrong;
how just and upright He is!

But we have acted corruptly toward Him;
when we act so perversely,
are we really His children?

Is this the way we repay the Lord,
we foolish and senseless people?
Isn't He our Father who created us?
Has He not made us and established us?

For the people of Israel belong to the Lord;
We are His special possession.
He found us in a desert land,
in an empty, howling wasteland.
He surrounded us and watched over us;
He guarded us as He would guard His own eyes.

But soon we became fat and unruly;

we grew heavy, plump, and stuffed!
Then we abandoned the God who had made us;
we made light of the Rock of our salvation.

We neglected the Rock who had fathered us;
we forgot the God who had given us birth.
The Lord saw this and drew back,
provoked to anger by His own sons and daughters."

"But God heard our cries, and He said:
Now I raise My hand to heaven
and declare, 'As surely as I live,
when I sharpen My flashing sword
and begin to carry out justice,
I will take revenge on My enemies
and repay those who reject Me.

I will avenge the blood of My children;
I will take revenge against My enemies.
I will repay those who hate Me
and cleanse My people's land.'

There is no one like the God of Israel.
He rides across the heavens to help us,
across the skies in majestic splendor.
The eternal God is our refuge,
and His everlasting arms are under us.
He drove out the enemy before us;
He cried out, 'Destroy them!'

So Israel, we now live in safety,
in a land of grain and new wine,
while the heavens drop down dew.
How blessed we are, O Israel!
Who else is like us, a people saved by the Lord?
He is our protecting shield
and our triumphant sword!
Our enemies cringe before us,
and He has stomped on their backs!"(1)

I then instructed the leaders to wash their clothing, their bodies, and purify themselves for worship. The next morning Uzzi opened the Book of the Law written by Moses and began to read what was written. When he finished, we all tore our garments and began to call out to Jehovah God in repentance.

Uzzi instructed us to bring seven bulls, seven rams, seven lambs, and seven goats – all unblemished – to be sacrificed as a sin offering. The offering was presented, and the animals' blood was sprinkled on the altar. There could be no forgiveness for our sin apart from the shedding of blood.

After the offering was complete, I led every leader in a pledge on behalf of the people to obey the Lord, with all our hearts and souls, by keeping His commands. We further pledged to remove all the detestable idols that had been erected throughout the land.

When we had done these things, I charged the leaders to gather their tribes and lead their people in a time of repentance, purification, and commitment. There would be no true peace if we did not first make our peace with our Lord. There would be no life without oppression until our people had completely abandoned their false worship and turned back to God.

He had been faithful to us … and now was our time to be faithful to Him.

With that directive, I sent out the leaders to return to their homes and lead their tribes to do as we had done!

~

24

A GOLDEN SHIELD

~

When Lappidoth and I, together with our fighting men, arrived back in Ai, we were greeted with shouts and cheers. The good news of God's victory had already made its way to the village long before our return. It was a joy to celebrate with our daughters and friends, and know that peace now dwelt throughout our land.

It was with great satisfaction that I returned to my place under the palm tree and began holding court again. Though the matters brought before me were important, they paled in comparison to the battles we had fought. I was often reminded that the same God who had faithfully led us to victory in times of war would lead us to walk victoriously in times of peace. I, in turn, reminded those who came before me that we must seek Him with the same earnestness no matter our circumstances.

I always began a judicial hearing this way: "Neighbors, you have come before me today to present your issue of disagreement. By doing so, you acknowledge I have been given judicial authority over all matters within the city of Ai, and, as of late, throughout all of Israel.

"You acknowledge I have been granted this authority by the elders of this village, by the elders of the tribes of Israel, and by Almighty God Himself. You join me in praying that Jehovah God will grant me His divine wisdom in evaluating the evidence you bring before me, and He will grant me the discernment to apply His wisdom when making my final decision. You agree to accept my judgment as the final word on the matter and to undertake whatever action I so adjudicate."

Regardless of the dispute, the parties coming before me needed to acknowledge my authority and agree to accept my verdict, whatever it might be, before we could proceed. Each side would then present their position of what had taken place.

Because I was the judge over all of Israel, I was in the unique position of hearing disputes from members of different tribes. If I had been only a local judge, I would have needed to be joined by at least two other judges – one from each tribe represented and one from a neutral tribe.

So, it was not unusual for people of different tribes from other parts of Israel to present their disputes before me. Such was the case between Joash of the tribe of Manasseh and Bechorath of the tribe of Benjamin. Both valiant warriors and tribal leaders, they had joined Barak and me in the attack against Sisera's army ten years earlier. They also were with us in Shiloh when we repented as a people before Jehovah God. I knew both to be honorable men.

Joash lived with his Abiezrite clan in the town of Ophrah. He brought his eldest son, Gideon, with him to help present his case. Bechorath lived in Gibeah with the Matrite clan. He also brought his eldest son, Zeror, to help present his case. Little did I know the implications our time under the palm tree that day would have on my family for generations to come.

Joash and Bechorath's cities are divided by the territory of the tribe of Ephraim. Gibeah is near my home in Ai and Ophrah is near the more northern town of Shiloh. As a matter of fact, their dispute started when we were all together in Shiloh following the victory in Hazor. Bechorath had somehow misplaced a golden shield that had been given to him by his grandfather. Joash had found the shield and, after trying unsuccessfully to find its rightful owner, had taken it back home with him.

For ten years, Bechorath had mourned the loss of his family treasure and was convinced the shield had been stolen. During those years, it had become the prized possession of Joash – one which he planned, upon his death, to pass along to his eldest son.

That would have been the end of the story if the two men had not recently encountered one another on their way to the tabernacle in Shiloh. Bechorath saw Joash carrying what he knew to be his shield. A dispute erupted, and neither man would calmly listen to the other. A few days later, they made the journey to Ai and now stood before me ready to plead their case.

I instructed each man to present his claim to me regarding the shield – first Bechorath, then Joash. Their sons were old enough to corroborate their fathers' stories. As the two men quietly listened to one another, it became obvious the shield rightfully belonged to Bechorath. Even Joash's son, Gideon, said, "Father, you must return this shield to this man. It is not yours to give to me; it is his to pass on to his son."

They hadn't really needed a judge to settle their dispute; they only needed to listen to one another. They apologized for having falsely accused each other and embraced as restored brothers and fellow warriors. I invited them to stay the night with Lappidoth and me so we could enjoy an evening meal together. That's when Gideon met my oldest daughter, Alya, and Bechorath's son, Zeror, met my younger daughter, Noya.

It became apparent before the night was over that both young men had more than a passing interest in my daughters – and my daughters were interested in them! I suppose stranger things have happened over the years to bring men and women together. In the case of these young men who would become my sons-in-law, all it took was a golden shield in the hands of a sovereign God!

~

25

A JUDGE TO FOLLOW

~

Forty years have now passed since our victory over King Jabin. Both my daughters are married: Alya and Gideon live in the village of Ophrah, Noya and Zeror live in Gibeah. God has blessed them both with many sons. Noya's oldest son, Abiel, is already married, and he and his wife recently gave birth to my first great-grandson, whom they named Kish.

Lappidoth and I had been married fifty-one years when he died three years ago; a part of me also died that day. Throughout our marriage he had supported me in my role as a judge of Israel. He had been my strength, my confidant, my encourager, and my wise counselor. His presence in my life was a continual reminder that God never calls us to serve Him without equipping us for the task. Lappidoth was an immeasurable part of God's equipping in my life.

But even more than that, he was my partner, my best friend, and the love of my life. I can't begin to tell you the number of times I have gone to turn to him for counsel and companionship over these past three years – only to be reminded he is no longer here. Gratefully, God has been right by my side to help me carry on. But I think I will be joining Lappidoth soon. I grow weaker each day, and I am experiencing great pains in my stomach. Those who have skills in treating such maladies are at a loss as to what more they can do for me. I have asked Jehovah God to continue to give me the days and the strength to finish all He has set before me to do.

Also, by the grace of God, there has been peace in the land these past forty years and our people have greatly prospered. For the most part, we have honored God in our worship and our actions. But I now find that many of our people no longer remember how Jehovah God saved us from the oppression of King Jabin. They no longer recall the death of General Sisera at the hands of Jael or the overwhelming victory over his army on the Kishon River plain or on the streets of Hazor. They have forgotten how we cried out to God for His forgiveness and committed to follow Him.

Instead, our people are now turning away from Him and pursuing their own ways. Many are turning to manmade gods and doing evil in the Lord's sight. Our history as a people reflects this same pattern time and again. God rescues us and we turn toward Him. In our prosperity, we turn away and grow further from Him. We ultimately reject Him and turn to evil. Our enemies see we no longer fear our God and they seize the opportunity to oppress and destroy us. Ultimately, we cry out to God in desperation, and He rescues us.

It has been this way throughout the 367 years since God delivered us from the slavery of Egypt. We repeatedly turned away from Him during our time in the wilderness and here in the Promised Land. And yet, through it all, He has continued to remember the covenant He made with Abraham, extending His mercy to us.

As of late, I have begun to hear reports that marauders from Midian and Amalek are attacking our southern tribes of Judah and Simeon, plundering their animals, and destroying their crops. The Amalekites have been our enemies since the day their warriors attacked our people at Rephidim in the wilderness. God gave us victory over them that day under the command of Joshua, as Moses stood with outstretched arms – assisted by

Aaron and Hur – on the hill overlooking the battle. But the hostility between our two peoples has continued to this day.

The Midianites were once our allies. Jethro, the Midianite father-in-law of Moses, helped our people during their journey through the wilderness. But even during the final days of Moses, the relations between our two peoples began to sour, and there has been strife ever since.

I fear the attacks by the marauders will increase in the days to come. As our people continue to pursue their evil ways, I fear the Lord will hand us over to them to seize our attention.

I no longer go each day to sit under the palm tree and judge the disputes between our people. I do not have the strength or physical ability to lead our people against these threatening enemies – and our people currently don't have the will to go up against them. But I am grateful to God there are men and women like Gideon, Alya, Zeror, and Noya that He will use to defeat our enemies and lead us back to Him in the days ahead. Perhaps He will choose one of them to become the next judge over Israel.

Last night as I lay in bed, I heard singing as if by a choir. I do not know where it was coming from, but the familiar words gave me hope:

"When Israel's leaders take charge,
and the people gladly follow –
bless the Lord, the God of Israel!

Listen, you kings!
Pay attention, you mighty rulers!
For we sing to the Lord.
We lift up our song to the Lord, the God of Israel.

Lord, when You set out from Seir
and marched across the fields of Edom,
the earth trembled and the cloudy skies poured down rain.
The mountains quaked at the coming of the Lord.

Even Mount Sinai shook
in the presence of the Lord, the God of Israel.

People avoided the main roads,
and travelers stayed on crooked side paths.
There were few people left in the villages of Israel –
until Deborah arose as a mother for Israel
to lead the people to follow the Lord, the God of Israel.

Then the people of the Lord
marched down behind her *to the city gates.*
Down from Tabor marched the remnant against the mighty.
The people of the Lord marched down against mighty warriors,
And followed the One who went before them – the Lord, the God of Israel.

Wake up again, O people of the Lord,
and again sing a song!
Rise like the sun at full strength
and return to Him,
and follow the Lord, the God of Israel."(1)

~

PLEASE HELP ME BY LEAVING A REVIEW!

i would be very grateful if you would leave a review of this book. Your feedback will be helpful to me in my future writing endeavors and will also assist others as they consider picking up a copy of the book.

To leave a review:

Go to: amazon.com/dp/1956866027

Or scan this QR code using your camera on your smartphone:

Thanks for your help!

~

YOU WILL WANT TO READ ALL OF THE BOOKS IN "THE CALLED" SERIES

Stories of these ordinary men and women called by God to be used in extraordinary ways.

A Carpenter Called Joseph (Book 1)

A Prophet Called Isaiah (Book 2)

A Teacher Called Nicodemus (Book 3)

A Judge Called Deborah (Book 4)

A Merchant Called Lydia (Book 5)

A Friend Called Enoch (Book 6)

A Fisherman Called Simon (Book 7)

A Heroine Called Rahab (Book 8)

A Witness Called Mary (Book 9) releasing March 24

A Cupbearer Called Nehemiah (Book 10) releasing June 16

Available in paperback, large print, and for Kindle on Amazon.

Scan this QR code using your camera on your smartphone to see the entire series.

THROUGH THE EYES

... the complete *"Through The Eyes"* Series

Experience the truths of Scripture as these stories unfold through the lives and eyes of a shepherd, a spy and a prisoner. Rooted in biblical truth, these fictional novels will enable you to draw beside the storytellers as they worship the Baby in the manger, the Son who took up the cross, the Savior who conquered the grave, the Deliverer who parted the sea and the Eternal God who has always had a mission.

Through the Eyes of a Shepherd (Book 1)

Through the Eyes of a Spy (Book 2)

Through the Eyes of a Prisoner (Book 3)

Available in paperback, large print, and for Kindle on Amazon.

Scan this QR code using your camera on your smartphone to see the entire series on Amazon:

~

THE EYEWITNESSES COLLECTION

... you will also want to read "The Eyewitnesses" Collection

The first four books in these collections of short stories chronicle the first person eyewitness accounts of eighty-five men, women and children and their unique relationships with Jesus.

Little Did We Know – the advent of Jesus (Book 1)

Not Too Little To Know – the advent – ages 8 thru adult (Book 2)

The One Who Stood Before Us – the ministry and passion of Jesus (Book 3)

The Little Ones Who Came – the ministry and passion – ages 8 thru adult (Book 4)

The Patriarchs — eyewitnesses from the beginning — Adam through Moses tell their stories (Book 5) — releasing in 2023

Now available through Amazon.

Scan this QR code using your camera on your smartphone to see the entire collection on Amazon:

LESSONS LEARNED IN THE WILDERNESS SERIES

The Lessons Learned In The Wilderness series

A non-fiction series of devotional studies

There are lessons that can only be learned in the wilderness experiences of our lives. As we see throughout the Bible, God is right there leading us each and every step of the way, if we will follow Him. Wherever we are, whatever we are experiencing, He will use it to enable us to experience His Person, witness His power and join Him in His mission.

The Journey Begins (Exodus) – Book 1

The Wandering Years (Numbers and Deuteronomy) – Book 2

Possessing The Promise (Joshua and Judges) – Book 3

Walking With The Master (The Gospels leading up to Palm Sunday) – Book 4

Taking Up The Cross (The Gospels – the passion through ascension) – Book 5

Until He Returns (The Book of Acts) – Book 6

The complete series is also available in two e-book boxsets or two single soft-cover print volumes.

Now available through Amazon.

Scan this QR code using your camera on your smartphone to see the entire series on Amazon:

For more information, go to:

wildernesslessons.com or kenwinter.org

ALSO AVAILABLE AS AN AUDIOBOOK

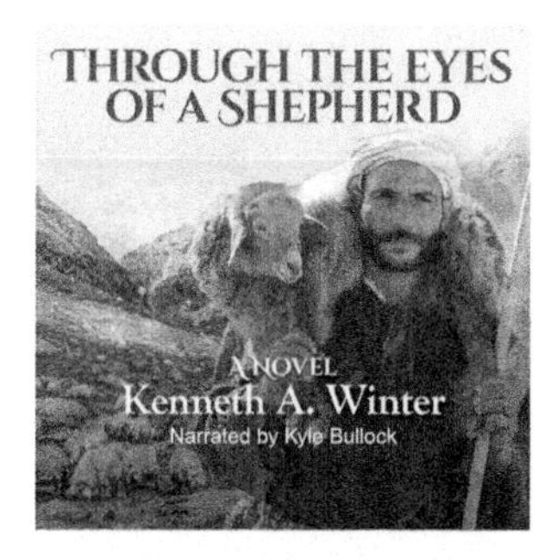

For more information on how you can order your audiobook, go to kenwinter.org/audiobooks

SCRIPTURE BIBLIOGRAPHY

~

Much of the story line of this book is taken from the Book of Judges. Certain fictional events or depictions of those events have been added.

Some of the dialogue in this story are direct quotations from Scripture. Here are the specific references for those quotations:

Chapter 1

(1) Judges 1:1

(2) Judges 1:2

(3) Judges 1:15

Chapter 2

(1) Deuteronomy 20:16-18

Chapter 5

(1) Joshua 6:26

Chapter 6

[1] Judges 3:19

[2] Judges 3:20

[3] Judges 3:28

Chapter 15

[1] Judges 4:6-7

[2] Judges 4:8

[3] Judges 4:9

Chapter 17

[1] Judges 5:2, 3, 5, 10, 12, 31

[2] Judges 4:9

Chapter 19

[1] Deuteronomy 32:35

[2] Judges 4:18

[3] Judges 4:19

[4] Judges 4:20

Chapter 21

[1] Judges 4:22

[2] Judges 5:24

Chapter 22

[1] Judges 5:3, 20, 21, 31

Chapter 23

(1) Deuteronomy 32:1-6, 9-10, 15, 18-19, 40-41, 43; 33:26-29

Chapter 25

(1) Italicized portions excerpted from Judges 5:2-31

~

LISTING OF CHARACTERS (ALPHABETICAL ORDER)

~

Many of the characters in this book are real people pulled directly from the pages of Scripture. i have not changed any details about those individuals except in some instances their interactions with the fictional characters. They are noted below as "UN" (unchanged).

In other instances, fictional details have been added to real people to provide additional background about their lives where Scripture is silent. The intent is to provide further information for the story. They are noted as "FB" (fictional background).

Lastly, a few of the characters are purely fictional, added to convey the fictional elements of these stories . They are noted as "FC" (fictional character).

~

Aaron – brother of Moses, first high priest of Israel (UN)
Abdon – father of Heber, ally of King Jabin (FC)
Abiel – son of Zeror, father of Kish (UN)
Achsah – daughter of Caleb, wife of Othniel (UN)
Alya – eldest daughter of Deborah and Lappidoth, wife of Gideon (FC)

Anath – son of Elad, father of Shamgar (FB)
Asa – brought dispute before Oded to be judged (FC)
Ayala – great-great-granddaughter of Othniel, wife of Ehud, mother of Elad (FC)
Barak – son of Abinoam, protégé of Shamgar, commander of army under Deborah (FB)
Bechorath – father of Zeror, brought dispute before Deborah (FB)
Bukki – son of Shesha, 6th high priest of Israel (UN)
Caleb – son of Jephunneh, one of the original twelve spies, elder of Judah (UN)
Cushan – son of King Jabin (1st), king of Aram, defeated by Othniel (FB)
Deborah – daughter of Oded, wife of Lappidoth, fourth judge over Israel (FB)
Eglon – king of Moab, defeated by Ehud (FB)
Ehud – son of Gera, husband of Ayala, father of Elad, second judge over Israel (FB)
Elad – son of Ehud and Ayala, father of Anath (FC)
Eleazar – son of Aaron, second high priest of Israel (UN)
Elias – brought dispute before Oded to be judged (FC)
Gera – father of Ehud, judge of Benjamin (FB)
Gideon – son of Joash, husband of Alya, fifth judge over Israel (FB)
Hathath – elder son of Othniel and Achsah (FB)
Heber – youngest son of Abdon the Kenite, husband of Jael (FB)
Hobab – son of Jethro the Midianite, Moses's wife's brother (UN)
Hur – Moses's sister's husband (UN)
Jabin (1st) – king of Hazor, defeated by Joshua (UN)
Jabin (2nd) – son of King Tirshi, king of Hazor, defeated by Barak (FB)
Jacob – brought dispute before Oded to be judged (FC)
Jael – wife of Heber the Kenite, mother of baby son – Joseph (FB)
Jethro – priest of Midian, father-in-law of Moses (UN)
Joash – father of Gideon, brought dispute before Deborah to be judged (FB)
Joseph – baby son of Jael (FC)
Joshua – son of Nun, Moses's assistant, second leader of Israel (UN)
Kish – son of Abiel, grandson of Zeror, father of King Saul (UN)
Lappidoth – husband of Deborah, father of Alya and Noya (FB)
Meonothai – younger son of Othniel and Achsah (FB)
Moses – adopted prince of Egypt, a shepherd in Midian, led Israelites out of Egypt (UN)

Noya – younger daughter of Deborah and Lappidoth, wife of Zeror, great-grandmother of King Saul (FC)
Oded – son of Shamgar, father of Deborah, judge of Ai (FC)
Ophrah – son of Meonothai, grandson of Othniel (UN)
Othniel – nephew and son-in-law of Caleb, husband of Achsah, first judge over Israel (UN)
Phinehas – son of Eleazar, third high priest of Israel (UN)
Saul – son of Kish, first king of Israel (UN)
Shamgar – son of Anath, father of Oded, third judge over Israel (FB)
Sisera – general over Hazorite army during the rule of King Jabin (2nd) (FB)
Thutmose II – son of Thutmose I, pharaoh of Egypt during time of exodus (UN)
Thutmose III – son of Thutmose II, pharaoh of Egypt after exodus (UN)
Tirshi – king of Hazor, rebuilt the city (FC)
Unnamed grandfather of Ehud – father of Gera, first tribal judge of Benjamin (FC)
Uzzi – son of Bukki, seventh high priest of Israel (UN)
Zeror – son of Bechorath and Noya, father of Abiel (FB)

~

ACKNOWLEDGMENTS

I do not cease to give thanks for you ....
Ephesians 1:16 (ESV)

... Sheryl,
for your help in telling the story in a far better way;

... Scott,
for the way you use your creative gift to bring glory to God;

... a phenomenal group of friends who have read an advance copy of this book,
for all of your help, feedback and encouragement;

... and most importantly,
the One who is truly the Author and Finisher of it all
– our Lord and Savior Jesus Christ!

~

ABOUT THE AUTHOR

Ken Winter is a follower of Jesus, an extremely blessed husband, and a proud father and grandfather – all by the grace of God. His journey with Jesus has led him to serve on the pastoral staffs of two local churches – one in West Palm Beach, Florida and the other in Richmond, Virginia – and as the vice president of mobilization of the IMB, an international missions organization.

Today, Ken continues in that journey as a full-time author, teacher and speaker. You can read his weekly blog posts at kenwinter.blog and listen to his weekly podcast at kenwinter.org/podcast.

And we proclaim Him, admonishing every man and teaching every man with all wisdom, that we may present every man complete in Christ. And for this purpose also I labor, striving according to His power, which mightily works within me.
(Colossians 1:28-29 NASB)

PLEASE JOIN MY READERS' GROUP

Please join my Readers' Group in order to receive updates and information about future releases, etc.

Also, i will send you a free copy of ***The Journey Begins*** e-book — the first book in the ***Lessons Learned In The Wilderness*** series. It is yours to keep or share with a friend or family member that you think might benefit from it.

It's completely free to sign up. i value your privacy and will not spam you. Also, you can unsubscribe at any time.

Go to kenwinter.org to subscribe.

Or scan this QR code using your camera on your smartphone:

~

Printed in Great Britain
by Amazon